61 Cooperative Learning Activities for Computer Classrooms

*Rachel Anderson and
Keith Humphrey*

J. WESTON
WALCH
PUBLISHER

PORTLAND, MAINE

User's Guide to *Walch Reproducible Books*

As part of our general effort to provide educational materials which are as practical and economical as possible, we have designated this publication a "reproducible book." The designation means that purchase of the book includes purchase of the right to limited reproduction of all pages on which this symbol appears:

Here is the basic Walch policy: We grant to individual purchasers of this book the right to make sufficient copies of reproducible pages for use by all students of a single teacher. This permission is limited to a single teacher, and does not apply to entire schools or school systems, so institutions purchasing the book should pass the permission on to a single teacher. Copying of the book or its parts for resale is prohibited.

Any questions regarding this policy or requests to purchase further reproduction rights should be addressed to:

Permissions Editor
J. Weston Walch, Publisher
321 Valley Street • P. O. Box 658
Portland, Maine 04104-0658

1   2   3   4   5   6   7   8   9   10
ISBN 0-8251-2838-2

Copyright © 1996
J. Weston Walch, Publisher
P.O. Box 658 • Portland, Maine 04104-0658

Printed in the United States of America

Contents

To the Teacher

Are you searching for computer activities for a middle school computer program for your classroom? If so, this book will be of value to you. *61 Cooperative Learning Activities for Computer Classrooms* contains plenty of exciting and challenging activities specifically designed so that students can work cooperatively. The activities are designed to work on any computer, so whether you have PC, Macintosh, or Apple II computers, this book has valuable lessons for all of your students.

61 Cooperative Learning Activities for Computer Classrooms consists of activities in the essential computer areas of **word processing, database, spreadsheet, drawing and painting, desktop publishing,** and **programming.** Also included are the timely topics of **CD-ROM, educational software, telecommunications,** and **multimedia presentation software.**

61 Cooperative Learning Activities for Computer Classrooms allows your students the opportunity to share ideas and work together, while using the computer as a tool, to accomplish a mutual goal. Imagine one member of a team searching for information on a CD-ROM encyclopedia while another member is using a modem to surf the Internet or bulletin board services to locate data. Envision a team using simulation software on one computer while entering their strategies into a word processing document on an adjacent computer. Observe students using a database to store and analyze a school survey or a spreadsheet to track stocks or profits from a bake sale. These are just a few of the 61 activities included in this book.

The student pages are reproducible. You can make as many copies as you need for the students in your classes. Meanwhile, you are not left out of this book, because the success of any lesson is equal to teacher input. Time is allowed for brief discussion and demonstrations before many of the hands-on activities. You will find many opportunities to introduce more difficult concepts. Each activity has a Teacher Guide Page with notes giving computer skills, student objectives, ability level, approximate time requirement, group size, materials needed, procedures to carry out the activity, and suggested evaluation methods. Also included with most activities are sections containing demonstration information and special tips (including additional notes, variations, and warnings). This information is provided to help guide you along a path to success with your students. But it is not the only approach. You are invited to modify the lessons to suit your style and class makeup.

Throughout our careers, we have been determined to find more ways of stimulating students' interest in all of their subjects. Two successful areas are cooperative learning and computer technology. The success of cooperative learning is improved if the teacher takes time to discuss group skills and dynamics. Pay attention to structuring the teams and assigning specific responsibilities to group members. The hardest parts of a cooperative learning lesson are planning and organization. *61 Cooperative Learning Activities for Computer Classrooms* is packed with exciting, well-planned, well-organized cooperative learning activities that will enhance your classroom lessons while allowing your students to participate in the technology revolution and learn to collaborate in task-related experiences.

It has been said that students can learn more from each other than they can from an adult and, at times, more from computers. Cooperative learning and computers—what a great combination!

CHAPTER 1

Word Processor

1. Shared Silly Nonsense Stories

Skills: **Word Processing**—starting a new document, editing, spell checking, block operations, saving and opening a file, and printing.

Objectives: To play a writing game in which word processing skills are utilized. To create a story through the use of small-group interaction.

Level: Beginning.

Time Required: One class period.

Group Size: Three or more students.

Materials Needed: One computer for each group, word processing software, and a printer.

Demonstrations Needed: A demonstration of this unique writing process may be required. Use a couple of volunteers to help write the first few lines of a story. Also, reviewing the block move operation that comes with your word processor could be useful if groups decide to move sentences around.

Procedure: Students create a story. Each member of the group enters two sentences. No other members of the group can watch as each person in the group enters her or his sentences. Only the second sentence appears on the screen for the next user. Each member of the group follows the same process until the entire story is entered. When the story is completed, the group deletes all the blank spaces between the sentences and reads over the story. Each group is allowed to use block operations to move sections of the story around so that it makes more sense. Students can print their completed story and read it to the class.

Evaluation: Evaluate students on the basis of group participation, the written composition, and the group presentation.

Special Tips: After forming the groups, make sure each group has typed in the introductory sentences. This helps the students get started and gives them some kind of direction for the story. You can make up your own introductory sentences if you wish.

Emphasize that students should not look at what another group member is typing. The fun in this game is the mystery. Remind the students to scroll down far enough so only one sentence is showing.

Watch the clock. You want to leave enough time for the students to edit their stories as well as present them to the class.

If the students are enjoying the game, you can always postpone the group presentations until the next class period.

Name _____ Date _____

Shared Silly Nonsense Stories

Why is your story going to be so silly? To begin with, you are going to write the story as a group. Each one of you will take turns writing two sentences. The tricky part is that you won't know what everyone else has written. Needless to say, the story comes out a little strange. Here's how it works:

1. In your group, decide who is going to be first, second, third, etc. Now, using one computer, run your word processing program. Create a new word processing file, and save it under the file name **NONSENSE**.

2. Read the following story introduction:

   Living in a small town was never easy for Tony. Face it! He was mischievous, and everyone in town knew it.

3. The first member needs to type this introduction into the word processor.

4. At this point, things become secretive. Without the rest of the group watching, the first group member types in her or his first sentence. Press **Enter** twice. Type the second sentence. Press **Enter** as many times as needed so that everything but the last sentence scrolls up and disappears.

5. It is now the second group member's turn. The only thing you should see on the screen is one sentence. How do you know what to write? You don't! Guess. This is what makes it fun and interesting. At least try to relate your sentences to the previous one. Type your first sentence. Press **Enter** twice. Write your second sentence. Press **Enter** so the only thing that appears on the screen is your second sentence. Pass on the computer to the next group member.

6. The rest of the group members take a turn. When everyone has had a turn, start all over. Your teacher will tell you when time is up. This is the end of your story.

7. Next, go back and take the blank spaces out of your story. There are a number of ways to do this. Can your group figure them all out? After deleting the spacing, spell check the document.

8. Now read the story. Does any of it make sense? Try moving some of the sentences around, putting them in a different order. (**Hint:** Use the Cut, Copy, and Paste commands.) Does your story make sense now? Probably not. Oh well! Save the story and get a printout.

9. Read your story out loud to the rest of the class. You'll hear nonsense from everyone else, too!

2. Magazine Mania

Skills: (1) **Word Processing**—starting a new document, editing, spell checking, saving and opening a file, and printing. (2) **Research**—current computer magazines.

Objectives: To collect and share useful information about computer technology.

Level: Beginning.

Time Required: Two class periods.

Group Size: Three to five students.

Materials Needed: Computer magazines (not too old), computers, word processing software, and a printer.

Procedure: Students research computer topics in current computer magazines. Once the groups are formed, each student selects a topic that no one else in the group has chosen. Each student researches the topic and writes a short essay and five quiz questions to ask the group. Each group member reads his or her essay to the group and then quizzes the group with the questions.

Evaluation: Evaluate students based on individual essays and quizzes.

Special Tips: The list of possible research subjects in the area of computer technology is extensive and ever-changing. Feel free to make additions and updates.

Allow time for group members to ask questions or share additional information.

Emphasize taking notes directly into the word processor. Review the use of Cut, Copy, and Paste commands.

Each student may share his or her information with the entire class.

Collect all the essays, and place them in a three-ring binder that is accessible to all students in all classes. Not only does this give each individual student a sense of importance, but also all students can use the information for future research.

If word processing software and/or computers are not accessible to all students, this project can be done with pen and paper.

To save time, instead of having each student ask his or her quiz questions, you can quiz each group as a whole. After all presentations are completed, use all the questions that group members generated.

Be aware that some students may either nonchalantly write the quiz or overemphasize the quiz. It is a nice feature to the project, but it can easily be dropped at your convenience.

Name _____ Date _____

Magazine Mania

Stop flipping through comic books, celebrity newspapers, and teenybopper magazines. Go high tech and surf through computer magazines. Today you are going to collect information from these magazines and pass that information along to your group members. Discover interesting facts about:

- CD-ROM
- bulletin board services
- educational software
- games
- Internet services
- computer graphics and computer art

- new information on personal computers
- new information on laptop computers
- computer viruses
- computer accessories
- people and computers (human interest stories)
- updates on computer and software companies

After you have formed a group, choose one of the above subjects or a subject of your own. Make sure no one else in your group has chosen the same subject.

Start paging through the magazines. Remember to take notes, using a word processor. When you have collected enough information, write a short essay. Use your editing skills to transfer information from your notes directly into your essay. This will save you time and energy. After completing the essay, write *five* quiz questions pertaining to your subject. Try not to make the questions too easy; your teacher will be grading them. And try not to make the questions too difficult; remember, you will be quizzed on all the other group members' subjects.

After completing the essay and the quiz questions, you are ready to present your research to the group. You may read your essay to the group, or your teacher may require you to print a copy for each group member. The next step is to quiz the group on your subject. Each group member in turn will present his or her research material and quiz. Upon completion, your teacher will collect the essays, quiz questions, and quiz results.

3. Jokes, Jokes, and More Jokes

Skills: **Word Processing**—starting a new document, editing, block operations, spell checking, saving and opening a file, and printing.

Objectives: To enter information (in this case, jokes) into individual documents and later merge the data from all of the documents into one word processing file.

Level: Beginning.

Time Required: One class period.

Group Size: Three or more students.

Materials Needed: One computer with word processing capabilities per student or per group and a printer.

Procedure: Each member of a group supplies the group with three jokes that are appropriate for school. Each member enters her or his three jokes into a new word processing document and saves the document on her or his own data disk. Once each member has completed the individual document, the group combines all the jokes into one master document, using the block copy feature. Then the group decides on the top five jokes, deletes all other jokes from the document, and moves the five jokes in an order from the least funny to the most funny. Finally, the group prints its five jokes and reads them to the class.

Evaluation: Evaluate students based on individual and group documents, group interaction, and group editing processes.

Special Tips: To save time, have students enter their three jokes as a homework assignment.

Have each student save her or his work on an individual data disk.

Check to make sure each student has created her or his own document. This will force the group to use more of their editing skills. Having a number of documents to work with makes the assignment more challenging.

Remind the students about the Cut, Paste, and Copy commands. The merging of all the jokes will take place within a group setting. Allow each group time to problem solve as a team, and thus figure out editing strategies themselves.

Review the concepts of opening multiple documents. With more than one document opened at a time, it becomes very easy to use the block copy command to copy the jokes from each member's document to the main document.

Create a class, grade, or school joke book. Students can help you collect and put together all the jokes. Ask the students to create a cover for the book by using drawing/painting software. This would be an excellent extra-credit project.

Try having students create a cartoon to match the joke.

Name _____ Date _____

Jokes, Jokes, and More Jokes

It's not a joke; this activity will sharpen your editing skills while you are telling jokes. All you have to do is write a few jokes and work with a group to solve editing problems. Each member of your group is responsible for supplying the group with three jokes that are appropriate for school and will not offend anyone. Here are the steps to follow:

1. Each student in the class must create a new word processing document and save it under a unique file name. In the document, write *three* jokes. If you are sharing a computer, make sure the next student creates her or his own document when you are done.

2. Now your teacher will place you in a group. The group's job is to figure out how to merge your jokes together into one document. Here is one way of completing the task:

   (a) Open each file containing jokes, and save the files on one disk.

   (b) With the disk containing all the jokes in the computer, create a new file and save it under the file name **JOKES**.

   (c) Open all the files containing jokes.

   (d) Using the Copy and Paste commands, copy the jokes from each member's document into the file **JOKES**. You can accomplish this by following these steps:

   • Select the text in one document.

   • Select the Copy command.

   • Display the **JOKES** document.

   • Move the cursor to where you want the jokes to appear.

   • Select the Paste command.

3. When the team jokes are all together in one document, select *five* of the best to represent the group. You may need to vote. Majority rules! Edit the group's document so that only the five selected jokes appear in the document. Use the block delete command to remove unwanted jokes. (Simply highlight the text you want to erase, and press the **Delete** key.)

4. Position the five jokes in order of the least funny to the most funny.

5. Before presenting your jokes to the rest of the students, explain to the class how you merged your jokes. What editing steps did you take to be successful? You may wish to elect a representative to explain to the rest of the class the procedures your group used.

6. Now, share your best jokes with the rest of the class. You may take turns reading the jokes, or you may elect a group representative to do the presentation.

7. Take a class vote. Which joke is the best?

4. Interview of a Lifetime

Skills: **Word Processing**—starting a new document, editing, block operations, spell checking, saving and opening a file, and printing.

Objectives: To conduct an interview, using the group process. To utilize word processing skills by taking notes throughout the interview and writing an essay about the interviewee.

Level: Intermediate.

Group Size: Three students.

Time Required: May vary from one to three class periods depending on the number of interviews as well as the depth of each interview.

Materials Needed: One computer for each group, word processing software, and a printer.

Procedure: Understanding the roles of the interviewing process is the key to this activity. One member of the group is responsible for interviewing another member, while the third member is entering the notes of the interview into a word processing document. On completion of the interview, all members of the group work on writing an essay about the interviewee.

Evaluation: Evaluate the students based on interviewing skills, group interaction, the notes, the final essay, and the presentation.

Special Tips: Make sure all of the questions asked are appropriate and are not embarrassing.

Make sure the interviewer creates a number of his or her own questions.

If at all possible, the writer should take notes directly onto the computer.

Encourage the use of the Cut, Copy, and Paste commands when the students are writing the group essay.

To extend this project, have the students switch roles within their group. Not only will this reinforce the interview process, but also each student will experience a new role and its duties. Of course, this will lengthen the amount of time needed for the activity. It would be fair to say one interview per class period.

If you have a limited number of computers, this activity could be done with pen and paper.

If your groups are larger than three students, more than one student could play the different roles. Partnership within a group setting is also a valuable cooperative learning experience. However, for this particular exercise, more than six students per group would be detrimental.

Name _____ Date _____

Interview of a Lifetime

In this activity you will play a role in the interviewing process. You will be the interviewee, the interviewer, or the writer. Being a part of an interview isn't always easy. The interviewee is often nervous and self-conscious, and the interviewer often depends on writers and editors to help produce the end product.

After your teacher has divided the class into groups, decide among yourselves the role each group member will play. Remember, you are working together to produce one end product; cooperation is key.

As an interviewee, your responsibilities include answering all the questions honestly and completely. In addition, be sure to speak slowly and clearly to allow for accurate note-taking.

As an interviewer, you are responsible for creating interesting questions to ask your subject. The following are a few questions to help you get started. Feel free to eliminate questions or add questions of your own to the list.

- Where and when were you born?
- Who are the members of your family?
- What has been the happiest or proudest moment in your life?
- What has been the saddest or most disappointing moment in your life?
- What is your favorite food?
- Who is your favorite actor, actress, musician, artist, etc.?
- What do you see yourself doing in five, ten, twenty years?
- If you had three wishes, what would they be?

As a writer, your responsibilities include taking notes directly onto the computer. Feel free to stop the interview and ask for clarification. Make sure your group members are speaking at a pace that is comfortable for your typing. After you have finished taking notes, organize them in an orderly fashion, using your word processing editing skills. Your teacher may ask you to make a copy of your notes for each of your team members.

Together, write an essay about the interviewee. Try to use some of the notes directly in the essay. This will save you the time and effort of having to retype. Be prepared to present your essay to the class.

5. A Book for Cooks

Skills: (1) **Word Processing**—starting a new document, editing, changing fonts and text styles (size, bold, italic, underline), justifying text (center, left, right), adding text frames, spell checking, saving and opening a file, and printing.
(2) **Research**—computer software or CD-ROM cookbooks, bulletin board systems, or the Internet.

Objectives: To create a cookbook using word processing software. To create a cookbook using small group interaction.

Level: Intermediate.

Time Required: Two class periods.

Group Size: Three to six students.

Materials Needed: Computer with word processing software and a printer. If possible, use computerized or CD-ROM cookbooks for student-conducted research.

Procedure: It's always a lot of fun having students log some of their favorite recipes. In this activity, each member of the group is responsible for bringing to class five of his or her favorite recipes. The group enters all the recipes into a word processing document, creating a well-organized cookbook. Also included with each cookbook are a table of contents and a cover page.

Evaluation: Evaluate students based on group interaction and final product.

Special Tips: The home economics teacher would be a great resource for this activity, or you could simply team-teach the project.

The recipe format includes a great deal of indentation. This may be a good time to introduce or review style sheets and page layout.

Remind students to use helpful word processing commands such as Cut, Copy, and Paste when arranging their recipes.

This activity promotes the use of telecommunications when researching recipes. While you might not have a modem connection in your classroom, many students do at home. Most of these students have a connection to a bulletin board system such as Prodigy, America Online, or CompuServe. Each of these services has a connection to the Internet, too.

Try putting together a class cookbook or even a school cookbook. Students could sell it to earn money for computer equipment and/or the computer club.

Have students create recipes that are about a topic being covered in a foreign language class or a social studies class (such as Greek, European, or English recipes).

Name _____   Date _____

A Book for Cooks

No one can deny it; everyone likes to eat. And what do you like to eat? What is your favorite snack? What is your favorite meal? Let's find out!

After your teacher has divided you into groups, discuss the type of cookbook your group would like to put together. Some cookbooks specialize in specific areas such as seafood, desserts, or Italian cuisine. However, most cookbooks are rather general, covering areas such as:

- appetizers and hors d' oeuvres
- soups
- salads
- breads

- main dishes
- desserts
- snacks

Whatever kind of cookbook your group decides to create, the work must be divided up equally. Each student is required to bring *at least five* recipes to the group.

Start looking for your favorite recipes at home in recipe boxes or cookbooks. Try looking in your school or public library. Ask a neighbor for great recipes. You could even try using a computer that has access to CD-ROM cookbooks, a bulletin board service, or the Internet.

The Ultimate Brownie Recipe

4 squares (1 ounce each) unsweetened chocolate
$\frac{1}{2}$ cup shortening
2 cups sugar
4 eggs
1 cup flour
1 teaspoon baking powder
1 teaspoon salt
1 cup chopped nuts

Yield: 32 brownies

Once you have collected your recipes, use word processing software to enter all the recipes into the computer. As a group, make sure the recipes are organized in a logical order.

Create a table of contents for your cookbook. As a group, vote on a title, and put together a cover that is well decorated.

Present the cookbook to your class and teacher. Each group member should discuss his or her favorite recipe. Mouths will water!

6. The Search for the Perfect School

Skills: (1) **Word Processing**—starting a new document, editing, changing fonts and text styles (size, bold, italic, underline), justifying text (center, left, right), adding text frames, spell checking, saving and opening a file, and printing.
(2) **Drawing and Painting** (optional).

Objectives: To write a classified ad as a group. To utilize word processing software.

Level: Intermediate.

Time Required: One class period.

Group Size: Three to six students.

Materials Needed: One computer with word processing software per group, a printer, and newspapers.

Procedure: Students write a classified ad that will help them search for the perfect school. Each group is responsible for the wording of the ad as well as the appearance.

Evaluation: Evaluate students based on group interaction and the final product.

Special Tips: Review with the students all the possible tools they could use to make their ad look more interesting.

Because this word processing activity is meant to look like an ad, the use of the different fonts, text styles, and the text frame is essential. You may want the students to experiment with these features before they get started.

Mention to your students that normally no more than two fonts are used on a page.

The students could write a classified ad about any of a number of different subjects, including a search for the perfect teacher, principal, school lunch, parents, sister, brother, soccer team, or toy.

Combine all the group ads, and create a classified ad page. Use desktop publishing software to lay out the ad page.

Display all the ads on one of your bulletin boards.

Name _____   Date _____

The Search for the Perfect School

Pretend to be a group of students who want to attend the *perfect* school. You can go anywhere in the world, and money is no object. However, you don't know where to start looking. You must advertise!

As a group, write a classified ad describing your idea of the perfect school. Your ad must catch the eye of the reader; no one looks at boring ads. Use your word processing software to spice things up. Use different fonts, text styles, text justifications, and text frames to make your ad stand out.

Remember, your classified ad must look the way it would appear in a newspaper. Take a look at some newspapers to get a better idea of what you are working toward. Don't forget to set your margins to make your ad appear in a column format.

Good luck! Hope you find what you are looking for.

Wanted: A School for Athletes!

The school must consider athletes first. All classrooms must be equipped with athletic equipment. The school must have a minimum of ten gymnasiums, two pools, six tennis courts, two training rooms, four racquetball courts, and one Olympic-sized indoor track. All school food must be of the highest quality. The principal and teachers must all be professional athletes.

Call 1-800-ATHLETE for more information.

---

7. Dear Student Advisor

Skills: **Word Processing**—starting a new document, editing, spell checking, block operations, saving and opening a file, and printing.

Objectives: To use word processing software to write and answer letters. To use small-group problem-solving skills.

Level: Beginning.

Group Size: Three to six students.

Time Required: Because the students are writing anonymous letters, you may wish to spread this assignment out over a week or two while the students are working on other projects. This will give the students the chance for some privacy at the keyboard.

Materials Needed: Independent access to a computer terminal for each student and, at times, one computer for each group. Word processing software and a printer. A network system is ideal for this activity. Students can send their letters back and forth over the network lines. If this is not possible, have the students print the letters, and you can play letter carrier.

Procedure: Each group in your class gives advice to their classmates. First, each group decides on a topic they feel comfortable with. Each group can only give advice on one topic, and no two groups can share a topic. Next, each student in the class writes a letter for advice using an anonymous name. Each letter is shown to the teacher (who doesn't read it) and then distributed to the appropriate advice group. All completed letters and advice are placed on a bulletin board for all students to view.

Evaluation: Evaluate students on the completion of a letter, group interaction, and group replies to the letters.

Special Tips: Some of the groups will receive more letters than others. Play this down as "no big deal." However, if the disparity is too great, have the groups share some of the letters. Every group should have at least two or three letters that need a reply.

If needed, review the procedures required to send files over the network.

Instead of allowing the groups to choose their own area in which to give advice, you may want to assign the topics. This will give you more control over the subject matter.

Some students may take this assignment as a joke. Simply collect those letters and do not allow the advice group to reply to them. In the end, the joking student will, more than likely, be disappointed that her or his letter is not up on the board.

Some students may take this assignment too seriously. They may use this forum as a way of calling out for help. Be prepared to offer it.

Dear Student Advisor

Advice from adults isn't what you always want. Sometimes the most welcome suggestions come from people your own age. But where can you get *anonymous* advice from fellow students? How about the computer room? That's right. You'll be able to find student advice right in your own computer room. How? From each other!

After your teacher has formed student groups, decide what kind of advice your group wishes to give. Here are some suggested topics for advice:

- money problems
- love
- relationships with parents
- relationships with sisters and brothers
- relationships with friends
- relationships with teachers

- subject areas (math, English, social studies, science, etc.)
- clothes
- what's "in" and what's "not in"
- peer pressure
- bullies

Once your group has decided on the type of advice you wish to give, inform your teacher. Your teacher will then post your group's choice as well as the other groups' choices. No two groups will be giving out the same type of advice.

Each student is required to write at least one anonymous letter to the advice group of her or his choice. Use your word processor to compose the letter. Give yourself a fake name like "Worried and Confused" or "Wishing for Love." You will get credit simply by showing the letter to your teacher. Don't worry; your teacher won't read it. Just a quick glance is all your teacher needs to establish the fact that you completed the assignment.

Next, send the letter to the advice group though the network. Make sure the name of your file does not give you away. If your school computers are not linked together, simply print your letter, place it in an envelope, address it to the appropriate advice group, and drop it on your teacher's desk.

After receiving your group's mail, discuss the letters and possible advice you wish to share. Divide the work up evenly, and reply to each letter. All group members should agree on the advice given; if not, offer more than one solution. Print the letter and your reply advice. Your teacher will post them on the bulletin board for everyone to see.

During free time, browse through other people's letters and advice as well as your own.

8. Future House

Skills: (1) **Word Processing**—starting a new document, editing, use of an outline style sheet, spell checking, saving and opening a file, and printing. (2) **Drawing and Painting** (optional).

Objectives: To use word processing tools, including style sheets. To work on an essay in a small-group setting.

Level: Intermediate.

Time Required: Two to three class periods.

Group Size: Three to six students.

Materials Needed: One computer with word processing capabilities per group and a printer. If students want to work independently on sections of this activity, you will need more computer terminals.

Demonstrations Needed: A demonstration using the outline style sheet may be needed. In addition, you may want to have examples of completed outlines. They could be on any subject. The students just need a general idea of what an outline looks like.

Procedure: Students create a detailed outline of what a future house might look like. Then, each group writes an essay describing their future house. Finally, each group presents their vision of a future house to the class.

Evaluation: Evaluate the students based on group interaction, the outline, the final essay, and the presentation.

Special Tips: Learning how to use a style sheet is an important step in word processing proficiency. It is unfortunate if your word processor does not have this tool. Yet it is still important for students to learn how to write and use an outline. Please require them to complete this step in the activity.

This is an excellent opportunity for you to work with the English teacher, when he or she is teaching outline format.

Drawing and painting tools would be perfect for creating a picture of the future house.

Students could write an essay on any of a number of futuristic subjects: future schools, future transportation, future clothes, future food, future sports, and so on.

Future House

When you're 50 years old, what will the modern house look like? Will houses be made out of wood, or will all the forests be gone? Will robots be doing the dishes, or will people still have to get their hands dirty? Will some people live in super high-rise apartment buildings like the Jetsons, or will some people live underground or under the sea? What do you think? In this activity you will get a chance to voice your opinion in a small-group setting.

Each small group is required to write an essay about the house of the future. First, you need to collect ideas. After your teacher has placed you in a group, sit and talk with your friends about the future. One of the group members should take notes directly onto the word processor. Remember, no ideas are too far-fetched, because no one can truly predict the future.

To help you organize your essay, as well as make it easier to divide the essay up into parts, you need to use an *outline*. Most word processors have an outline style sheet. Use this tool. If you do not have access to style sheets, create an outline according to your teacher's specifications.

Show your outline to your teacher before writing the essay. Once your teacher has approved your group's outline, begin writing. Use word processing software. You may work together or alone. If you work independently, make sure the work is divided equally among group members. Hand the group outline and essay in to your teacher for grading purposes.

Present your ideas to the class, emphasizing the most interesting concepts. After all of the groups have presented their ideas, vote on which house you would most like to live in.

9. The Thesaurus Twist

Skills: **Word Processing**—starting a new document, editing, spell checking, thesaurus, saving and opening a file, and printing.

Objectives: To change a story by using the thesaurus. To work with the thesaurus in a small-group setting.

Level: Intermediate.

Time Required: Two class periods.

Group Size: Three to six students.

Materials Needed: One computer per group. Word processing software with thesaurus search/replace capabilities. A printer.

Demonstration Needed: A demonstration of basic thesaurus features would be helpful.

Procedure: One of the most forgotten yet useful word processing features is the thesaurus. Students shy away from it because they think it is too hard to use, or the word *synonym* scares them. This activity exposes students to the playfulness of synonyms. In a group setting, students transcribe a children's story into the word processor. Once the story is in place, they start manipulating it by using the thesaurus. Each student must replace five words within the story with a thesaurus synonym. They will soon realize that synonyms are not always the *same*.

Evaluation: Evaluate students based on group participation, thesaurus use, final product, and the presentation.

Special Tips: Make sure the stories the groups choose are long enough. It is frustrating for the students when they can't find any interesting words to replace. In the long run, they are better off with a longer story. Besides, transcribing is good keyboard practice.

Make sure the group members take turns replacing words. This way, no one can complain, "Natasha used up all the good words" or "There aren't any good words left for Mark and me."

Remind the students that some of the best words to change are adjectives, better known as descriptive words. In addition, adjectives usually have a number of synonyms to choose from.

Name _____ Date _____

The Thesaurus Twist

What if the "big bad wolf" had really been the "generous decayed canine"? The whole story would have been different or maybe even twisted. Yet the word *generous* is a synonym for *big*, *decayed* is a synonym for *bad*, and *canine* is a synonym for *wolf*. Then why has the meaning changed so much just by using synonyms?

A thesaurus is a powerful tool. It gives a writer access to new and interesting vocabulary. Using a thesaurus can add excitement as well as detail to your compositions. At the same time, a thesaurus can be dangerous. Some synonyms may change the whole meaning of what you are trying to say.

This activity is designed to demonstrate the power of a thesaurus. Each member of your group brings a children's story to class. The story should be *at least 300 words* in length. As a group, look at all the stories. Vote on which one you would like to "twist." The story should be familiar to all, and it should have enough description to twist. Ask your teacher for approval and then begin twisting.

This is how you twist:

1. Transcribe the story on the word processor. Everyone should take a turn copying a part of the story. This can be boring work; if you work together, it will go by quickly.

2. Once you have a copy of the story in the word processor, the fun begins. Each member of the group is responsible for changing *at least five* words in the story. The *only* way you are allowed to change a word is by using the thesaurus.

3. Use the Search/Replace feature of your thesaurus. You *must* use one of the synonyms offered by the thesaurus. If it changes the meaning, you have a "twist."

4. Take turns changing one word at a time. The rest of the group may make suggestions or cheer you on, but the final word decision is yours.

5. One group member is not allowed to change a word already changed by someone else.

6. Once everyone in the group has changed five words, check to see if you have more time. If so, keep going until time is up.

7. Save your new story under another file name.

For twisted fun, take turns reading your new twisted story to the rest of the class. Print a copy of the original as well as the twisted story for your teacher to grade.

10. Right, Wrong, or Weird

Skills: **Word Processing**—starting a new document, editing, spell checking, thesaurus, saving and opening a file, and printing.

Objectives: To use a word processor's thesaurus in a game-playing setting. To use small-group cooperation to write an essay.

Level: Advanced.

Group Size: Three to six students.

Time Required: Two class periods: one for the essay writing and one for the game playing.

Materials Needed: One computer with word processing capabilities and one thesaurus per group. This is an ideal network activity; the students could exchange their essays over the network. If not, students will need disks to download their files and exchange. If you wish, each group may use more than one computer. Just make sure each group has the same number of computers.

Demonstration Needed: A demonstration of thesaurus use may be helpful.

Procedure: Small groups write a descriptive essay. Each group then removes 20 words from the essay and replaces them with numbers. The removed words are collected in list form. Students add 20 "wrong" or "weird" words to the list. A different group receives their numbered essay and 40-word list and tries to replace the original words. The only tool the students are allowed to use to assist them is the computer's thesaurus.

Evaluation: Evaluate students based on group interaction, the original essay, and the timely finish of the word find exercise.

Special Tips: Groups can exchange essays over the network or by disk.

For game fairness, all essay exchanges should take place at the same time. No one group should start working on the word find before all the others have received their essays.

All groups must finish the activity even after the first group has finished and won.

Have students boldface or underline the "wrong" or "weird" words used in the essay.

Remind students to keep their descriptions appropriate to a classroom setting.

Name _____ Date _____

Right, Wrong, or Weird

As a group, write a descriptive essay about your computer technology room. Choose obvious items to describe—for example, the computers, the bulletin boards, the tables, the teacher, the students. Or choose more obscure items—for example, the fire alarm, the gum underneath your desk, the computer cables and wires, the ceiling, the skid marks on the floor.

Whatever you choose to write about, the essay must be *at least 300 words* in length. If your word processor has a word count feature, use it to total the number of words in your document. Be as descriptive as possible, using numerous adjectives and adverbs. Try writing the essay together as a group. Or divide the work by assigning items to describe and combining the work into one essay later.

Once you have finished your group essay, save it as the original file. Now, start taking the most interesting words out of the essay and replacing each one with a number. Create a list of the removed words on another page or in a separate file. These are easy tasks if you remember to use editing tools such as Cut, Copy, and Paste. Remove 20 words from your essay.

At this point, you should have an essay with 20 numbers in it and a list of 20 removed words. These words are obviously the "right" words. Now, to this list add "wrong" or "weird" words. Use your thesaurus to come up with similar words or outlandish words. Add and mix 20 "wrong" or "weird" words to your original list. Your new list should have 40 words.

When you have finished your list, exchange your numbered essay and "right," "wrong," or "weird" word list with another group. The object of this activity is to attempt to return another group's essay to its original state. The first group to do so wins! The restrictions are:

- Only use words from the "right," "wrong," or "weird" list.

- Changes must be made on a word processor.

- Use only the computer's thesaurus. You may not use printed dictionaries or thesauruses.

- Once you believe you have replaced the words correctly, check with the other team. They *must* correct your paper in a timely manner and inform you which answers are wrong. (While one group member is correcting a paper, the rest of the group should still be working on the other essay.)

When you have all the correct words in place, you're done! Which group was the first?

CHAPTER 2

Database

11. Movie Critics

Skills: **Database**—entering information into a database, sorting records by a field type, searching for records in a database by entering a text or numeric criteria, and displaying records on the screen in a list or column format.

Objectives: To expose students to basic uses of a database. To use a database to collect data about movies. To use cooperative learning in data collection and data analysis.

Level: Beginning.

Time Required: Two to three class periods.

Group Size: Three to six students.

Materials Needed: At least one computer per group. Individual computers for each team member would be helpful for the opinion data collection. A database created by the teacher.

Demonstrations Needed: Show students how to enter data into a record, advance the database to a new record, search for records of a common type by using text or numeric search options (including searches on multiple fields), and display records in a list or column format. Stress the importance of entering data consistently and accurately.

Procedure: Most students love movies, and they love to talk about them with friends. In this activity, students act as movie critics. Using a database, they collect and analyze data about movies.

Students collect information about *five* movies, enter that data into an existing database, and answer questions about the records by searching the database and displaying records in a list and column format on the screen. You need to create the actual database.

Evaluation: Evaluate students based on group participation, group analysis, individual opinions, and the group presentation.

Special Tips: Save the databases as a reference tool, possibly merging them into one class database or even a multiclass schoolwide database.

A number of movie critics' articles are posted on bulletin board services. You may wish to download an example for the students to look at and model.

Have the groups meet initially to decide what movies they want to work on, and then to assign each member a movie or two. Allow students a few days to find the general information. The description paragraph should be worked on as a group.

Students may use this same database concept to critique music albums, concerts, theater performances, novels, and so on.

Ask each group to search for the answer to one of your questions. Have the results displayed on the screen in a list format.

Name _____ Date _____

Movie Critics

Siskel and Ebert are two very famous movie critics in the United States today. If you have ever watched their television show, you will notice how they work together to give the audience a general overview and solid opinions of recent movies. Even when they disagree and argue, they never give a wimpy critique; you always know how they feel about the movie.

In this activity, you and your group will play the roles of the movie critics. Using a database, you will collect facts, thoughts, and opinions about the movies of your choice. Each group is responsible for analyzing *five* movies. All group members must have seen the movie. Choose movies you disliked as well as ones you liked.

Step 1: Collecting the General Data About Each Movie

As a group, complete the following general information about each movie. The first section asks for a name for your critics' group. The remaining fields have to do with the movie.

1. Name of your group
2. Name of movie
3. Year produced
4. Name of director
5. Name of leading actor
6. Name of leading actress
7. Type of movie (action, comedy, animated, romantic)
8. Academy of Motion Pictures rating (G, PG, PG-13)
9. One-paragraph description of the movie

Step 2: Collecting Each Member's Opinion Data About Each Movie

The next data collection section must be filled out by individual members. Do not work as a group to answer these questions. The questions are based on opinion, and it is important to hear from each individual. Each member should write down the names of each movie for the group and complete the following personal opinions for each movie.

1. Would you give this movie a "thumbs up" or "thumbs down"?
2. Number rating 1–10 (1 being the worst and 10 being the best).
3. One-paragraph opinion about the movie.

Step 3: Entering the Data into the Database

Now that your group has all the movie information, the next step is to enter it into the database created by your teacher. Be sure to enter each field with the exact words that are appropriate for the given field. For example, always use the phrase "thumbs up" or "thumbs down" in the personal opinion field. Don't enter "thumbs up" for one record and "up" for another; this

(continued)

Movie Critics (continued)

kind of inconsistency will throw off the validity of your data. Each member of the group should enter one complete record, which is made up of the general data and the opinion data. Therefore, when all records are entered, the total number of records you should have is five times the number of members in your group. If you have four members, then there should be twenty records.

Hint: Rewriting the paragraph description can become tedious. See if your database program will allow you to copy a paragraph from one record and enter it into another. Most Windows and Macintosh software will allow you to use the Copy/Paste feature found in the Edit menu to move text from one record to the clipboard and then to another record.

Step 4: Analyzing All Records in Your Databaes

Now that you have collected all the important data, it is time to analyze and draw conclusions from the information you have collected. Below are five important analysis questions to ask your database. Your job is to find the answers to the five questions shown below and create five additional questions. Write down the additional questions along with the answers for each.

To find the answers, try sorting the records by a field and displaying the records in a list or column format. Study the list to find the answer to each question. Another approach is to enter a specific word or phrase (such as "thumbs up") or a number or numeric expression (such as 10 or >9) to search for. Display all records that contain the search criteria in a list format.

1. How many movies received a rating of a 10 from the group?

2. How many times did your groups rate a movie a 10?

3. Who starred in the lowest 1–10-rated movie?

4. Which type of movie received the most "thumbs down" ratings from the group?

5. Who directed the highest 1–10-rated movie?

Once your data analysis is complete, present the results to the class. Read the general description of the movie if needed. Also read *at least one* opinion paragraph about each movie.

After the group presentations, your teacher will save all the collected data from all the groups and classes. This will make it convenient for research purposes and simple curiosity. If you are wondering about a particular movie you haven't seen yet, simply look it up in the database. You'll be able to read a description as well as a thorough critique of the movie. The database is your own *Siskel and Ebert* at your fingertips!

12. Student-Generated Encyclopedia

Skills: **Database**—entering information into a database, sorting records by a field type, searching for records in a database by entering a text or numeric criteria, and displaying records on the screen in a list or column format.

Objectives: To use a database to collect information for a student-generated encyclopedia. To use research tools. To use cooperative learning as a way to collect and organize data.

Level: Beginning.

Time Required: Five class periods.

Group Size: Three to six students.

Materials Needed: One computer per group, or one computer for data collection and another for data entry. A teacher-created database.

Demonstrations Needed: Show students how to enter data into a record, advance the database to a new record, search for records of a common type by using text or numeric search options (including search on multiple fields), and display records in a list or column format. Stress the importance of entering data consistently and accurately.

Procedure: Students generate their own encyclopedia by using a database. Students collect and enter data into an existing database created by the teacher. Every member of a group researches and enters two records into the database. The goal is to have one common database at the end of the activity that contains every record from each group. The groups can enter their records into one common database or into separate databases which are then merged. Students end the activity by searching through the common database, called the class encyclopedia database, for answers to problems you create. Other students can now use the class encyclopedia database as a research tool. Students can easily expand and add to it so it becomes a school-wide resource, as explained on the student pages.

Evaluation: Evaluate students based on group participation, research techniques, database entry, and the final critique.

Special Tips: When approving a subject area, make sure the subject isn't being done or hasn't been done previously by another group in this or another class.

Create a field structure for the database as a class. Show students on the board how a database is made up of specific fields. Ask for student suggestions for types of fields needed.

Surf the Internet for other schools generating encyclopedias. Maybe a combined effort would not only be beneficial but also fun for the students.

Student-Generated Encyclopedia

Have you ever wondered who writes encyclopedias? What often comes to mind is a bunch of old guys with beards sitting around paging through books. Or a bunch of old ladies with glasses writing with feather pens and parchment paper. Well, times have changed. Writing an encyclopedia is much easier, and the process is much faster, since the dawn of the computer and the database. Even students can write an encyclopedia well and quickly; you're going to prove it in this activity.

Step 1: Selecting a Topic

After your teacher has divided you into groups, decide which encyclopedia subject area your group wants to research and write about. Each group will choose a general subject area different from the other groups. This way, you will have very little overlapping of information. Of course, you do not have to cover the *whole* subject area. For example, if you choose Life Science, your group may decide to write about animals, more specifically mammals, and even more specifically apes. These are the general encyclopedia subject areas:

- Art, Language, and Literature
- Geography
- History
- Life Science
- Performing Arts

- Physical Science and Technology
- Religion and Philosophy
- Social Science
- Sports, Games, and Hobbies

Step 2: Collecting the Facts

After you have chosen a subject area and your teacher has approved it, start collecting interesting facts about your subject for the database. Each member of the group is required to have *two* completed records to add to the database.

You can conduct your research in a number of different ways. Use conventional reference materials like encyclopedias, atlases, periodicals, subject-based books, and textbooks. Use computer technology like CD-ROM software, bulletin board services, and the Internet. Finally, use experts—interview people who know a great deal about your subject.

Your group can divide the work by subcategories. For example, the subject of apes could be divided by the different types of apes: chimpanzees, gorillas, orangutans, and so on. Or if you all wanted to study gorillas, the work could still be divided: habitat, food, general description, behavior, mating, offspring, and so on. However, in the end, the *group* is responsible for the whole project.

(continued)

Student-Generated Encyclopedia *(continued)*

Step 3: *Entering the Information into the Encyclopedia Database*

When you have finished your research, start entering the data into the database. The database, set up by your teacher, may ask for general information first and then a paragraph or two about your subject.

Step 4: *Searching the "Class Encyclopedia Database"*

As the final part of this assignment, search through a database that contains all records from each group to find answers to questions that your teacher has generated. This database is called the class encyclopedia database. If each group has been entering their records into a common database, then the class encyclopedia database is already completed. If each group has been entering records into separate databases, then your teacher will merge all class records into the class encyclopedia database.

Now you and other students can use the class encyclopedia database as a research tool. You can expand it during the school year as your group works on new topics. It will become one huge database. Additions can be made on a yearly basis as well. In no time at all, it will become a comprehensive and effective encyclopedia for everyone in your school to use.

You might even think about having a copy on the computer in the school library.

13–14. Ask and Analyze

There is nothing on earth students are more curious about than each other. Public opinion is very important to the average middle school student. For this reason, student surveys are very popular activities. Students are able to ask questions they've been dying to ask, yet the questioning is conducted in a safe and welcoming environment.

This activity is made up of two parts: conducting a survey and analyzing a survey. First, the students formulate the survey questions themselves, creating a list in a small-group setting. Survey questions are answered by the students themselves along with other students in the school.

In the second activity, small groups of students analyze the results of the survey. They make queries and attempt to draw conclusions. In the end, the students write a group outcome essay and prepare for a class discussion on the survey and the results.

13. Ask and Analyze: Part I— The Survey

Skills: (1) Database—completing a survey, creating a database by defining field size and attributes, and entering information into a database. (2) Word Processing—starting a new document, editing, spell checking, saving and opening a file, and printing.

Objectives: To create a database to store information from a group's student survey. To conduct a survey through the use of small-group and large-group cooperative learning.

Level: Intermediate.

Group Size: Three to six students.

Time Required: Two class periods for writing and combining the survey questions. Conducting the survey itself can take place outside of the classroom and over a longer period of time. Two additional days are needed to enter the records into the database.

Materials Needed: One computer per group with word processing and database capabilities. One computer per class with the database up and running.

Demonstrations Needed: Show students how to enter data into a record, advance the database to a new record, search for records of a common type by using text or numeric search options (including search on multiple fields), and display records in a list or column format. Stress the importance of entering data consistently and accurately.

Procedure: Students create a database to store information from a survey they conduct. Each group formulates 25 survey questions about their peers by brainstorming and entering the questions into a word processing document. The 25 survey questions are handed in to the teacher for approval. Upon approval, each group completes 50 surveys, with this work divided among all the group members. Once the survey is complete, the group designs a database with 25 fields (one for each question) and enters all the records. The database file is handed in to the teacher along with the 50 survey forms.

Evaluation: Evaluate students based on small-group as well as large-group interaction and on the questions generated by their group, the design of the database, and the entering all of the required 50 records.

Special Tips: Students should understand that they will conduct the survey outside of class. Home-room and lunch periods are perfect times to complete the surveys. Each group could be responsible for getting 50 surveys completed by their friends. The 50 surveys should be divided among all group members.

Be sure to look over the 25 questions each group comes up with. Collect a printout of all surveys before allowing the students to begin the survey. What you approve should match the 25 fields created in the database.

Collect the handwritten surveys along with the database file. Mention that you will randomly compare a few surveys with the database to make sure students have accurately entered the records.

Ask and Analyze: Part I—The Survey

In your school, most of the students prefer chocolate ice cream over vanilla. The favorite sport boys like to play is shuffleboard, and the favorite sport girls like to play is soccer. The best school lunch is meat loaf, and the worst school lunch is pizza. The students' favorite type of music is rock and roll, and the favorite teacher is the technology teacher.

How many of these statements are true? How many of these statements are false? And how do you know? One of the best ways to find the answers to these questions and others is to conduct and analyze a student survey. Some of the results you may expect, but others may surprise you.

The first step in conducting a survey is actually to write the survey. After your teacher has placed you in a group, start discussing the possible questions you would like to ask your fellow students. Each survey must have 25 questions. The following seven questions are required for all surveys:

- What is your birth date?

- Where were you born?

- How old are you now?

- What grade are you in?

- Are you a male or female?

- What is your estimated grade point average?

- What is your cultural heritage or ancestry (Italian, African, German, Native American, etc.)?

As a group, come up with the remaining 18 questions. Some possible questions you might ask in the survey are:

- Who is your favorite music group?

- What is your least favorite chore to do at home?

- What is your favorite subject in school?

- Do you plan to attend college?

- What is your weekly allowance? (If you do not have an allowance, answer zero.)

Write your 25 group-compiled questions on a computer, using word processing software. Hand the list in to your teacher. Once your questions are approved, go out and complete 50 surveys. Divide the work among all group members, and make sure to put your name on each survey. During class, create the database to store all 50 records. Once all 50 records are logged into the database, hand in to your teacher the database file and all the survey forms.

14. Ask and Analyze: Part II— Survey Analysis

Skills: (1) **Database**—sorting records by a field type, searching a database by entering search criteria in one or more fields, and creating a report in list or column format and displaying it on the screen. (2) **Word Processing**—starting a new document, editing, spell checking, saving and opening a file, and printing.

Objectives: To analyze the student survey through the use of queries. To analyze the student survey through the use of small-group and large-group discussions.

Level: Intermediate.

Time Required: Two to three class periods.

Group Size: Three to six students. The same groups as in Part I.

Materials Needed: One computer per group with database and word processing capabilities. Two computers would be ideal: one computer to analyze the database and the second computer to type conclusions in a word processing document.

Demonstrations Needed: Show a few examples of text and numeric searches that include searches on multiple fields.

Procedure: Once the survey database is created and all records are entered, each group can decide on the types of questions to answer by searching their database. Each group types 10 questions in a word processing document that will be of interest to the class. Each member of the group practices searching skills and finds the answers to all ten questions. The answers are added to the existing word processing document and later turned into an essay that describes the students' opinions on the findings. Their findings and opinions are presented to the class at the end of the activity.

Evaluation: Evaluate students based on small-group interaction, the written queries, the outcome essay, and the presentation.

Special Tips: Have each group present their database in front of a computer with a large-screen monitor. As each group completes their presentation prepared from the word processing document, allow other students to ask the group to do a particular search. The group is responsible for generating the search. This will add time to the presentation, but it will allow the audience to participate while giving each group a chance to display their search techniques.

Name _____   Date _____

Ask and Analyze: Part II—Survey Analysis

Analyzing your survey may answer a number of nagging questions you have had about your friends and peers. But analyzing a survey is more than just looking at the numbers. You need to ask the database questions, or *queries*. As a group, brainstorm for possible queries. The following are examples of queries you might use:

- Which musical group is the most popular with the girls?

- How many students are left-handed?

- If all the students pooled their allowances for one week, how much money would that be?

Write down or record in a word processing document *at least 10* interesting queries. Complete database searches by entering specific information in one or more fields. Display the searches in a list or column format to understand the results better. Log the answers to each question on a printout that contains the questions, or type them directly into the word processing document. If available, use a second computer to enter the results in the word processing document while viewing the database reports on the original computer.

After the results are tallied, as a group, analyze the survey, the queries, and the results. In a short essay, explain how your group feels about the survey process and the results. This is known as an *outcome essay*. How did the outcome of the survey influence you? Which results surprised you? Which results were no surprise? Which questions and answers turned out to be the most interesting? Which questions and answers turned out to be a big flop?

After writing your essay, be prepared to discuss your outcome essay. Your teacher will lead a class discussion about the survey and the results.

15–16: Television Violence

Television violence is an issue that concerns adults but, oftentimes, not young people. Young people see so much violence that they may simply not be aware of it. This activity is designed to heighten awareness through the use of a database.

This activity is made up of two parts: data collection and data analysis. Students collect data for one week using a Data Collection Sheet (located after the student instructions) to record the violence they witness. As a group, they create a database and enter all of their combined data into the database. Each record in the database represents one show viewed. After all the records are entered, each group is required to sort the data by the Day field and print it in a list or column format.

In the second activity, the students analyze the database results. They make queries on the database and attempt to draw conclusions. In the end, the group writes an analysis essay and presents their findings to the rest of the class.

15. Television Violence: Part I— Data Collection

Skills: **Database**—completing a data collection sheet, creating a database by defining field size and attributes, entering information into a database, sorting records by a field type, creating a report in list or column format (with labels and possibly footers and headers, adjusted margins, and smaller font sizes), previewing and printing a report.

Objectives: To learn about TV violence through the use of group data collecting and analysis. To learn about the usefulness of a database.

Level: Advanced.

Group Size: Three to six students.

Time Required: One week of data collection and two to three days to create the database, enter all the records, and generate a report in list or column format.

Materials Needed: At least one computer per group with database software and a printer.

Procedure: Each member of a group completes a TV violence form while watching TV over a one-week period. A data collection sheet is included in the student materials. Students record the number and type of violent acts during the show and commercials. After completing the data sheet, students review each other's lists for overlapping viewings and record the averages for these shows. As a group, they create a database and enter all their combined data into it. Each record in the database represents one show viewed. After all the records are entered, each group sorts the data by the Day field and prints it in a list or column format. The printout and the survey forms are stapled together and handed in to you.

Evaluation: Evaluate students based on group participation and the final data collected.

Special Tips: Students should understand how to create a database by defining field lengths and attributes (numeric or character).

Make sure to preview the printouts before each group prints. Look to see that the printout is formatted in list or column format with labels that include a title and the names of all members in the group. Many times students will print all the records in a form format that prints each record on a separate sheet of paper. That's a lot of paper and a long bottleneck at the printer.

Collect television-related data on different subjects such as negative language, positive images, sexist or racist remarks or images, or appearance of alcohol. Collect radio-, magazine-, or newspaper-related data.

You can have your class complete this activity without doing Part II. In place of having students write the Part II essay, have each group spend a few minutes sharing with the class the conclusions they came up with from the survey they completed and the printed report of all the records in the database.

Name _____ Date _____

Television Violence Data Collection Sheet

Have you ever wondered how much violence you and your family watch on television? How much violence do you see watching prime-time comedies? How much violence does your little brother or sister see watching those cute little cartoons? How much violence do your parents see watching a late-night movie? Most people see so much violence on TV that they aren't even aware of it. This activity is designed to increase your awareness of TV violence.

What do you consider a violent act? *Webster's Dictionary* defines violence as "physical force used to injure or damage; assault." So when Tom the cat hits Jerry the mouse with a frying pan, is this violence? Yes. How about when Lassie bites the bad guy? Is this violence? Yes. What about a character in a comedy falling down a flight of stairs? Is this violence? No. However, if he were pushed down the steps, that would be violence.

Type of Violence: **G**—gun
                W—other weapon
                H—hand to hand

Day	Name of Show	Network	Viewing Time	# of Violent Acts in a Show			# of Violent Acts in a Commercial			Total
				G	W	H	G	W	H	

(continued)

Television Violence: Part I—Data Collection *(continued)*

Complete the chart as you watch television. Record the violence you witness on TV by writing down a vertical line (||||) or a number in the columns with G, W, or H every time you see a violent act of that type in the TV show or the commercials shown during that show. Record days of week using the labels SUN, MON, TUE, WED, THU, FRI, and SAT. Also, when entering the names of the shows in the database, be sure to type each name exactly the same each time. This will become very important when you need to search for a particular show. The Total column represents the number of violent acts you saw during the time you watched the show (including commercials).

Step 1: Collecting the Data

The first step in an investigation of TV violence is to collect data. After your teacher has placed you in a group, look over the data collection sheet. For one week, whenever you watch television, you will record the number of times you witness a violent act.

For data-collecting purposes, violence is divided into three different types. The first type is violence with a gun (G). The second type is violence with any other kind of weapon (W)—for example, a frying pan, a sword, a rubber chicken, a knife. The third type is hand-to-hand violence (H)—for example, fighting, pushing, scratching, biting.

On your data collection sheet, record the day you watch the show, the name of the show, the name of the network, the viewing time, the number of violent acts by type for the show and the commercials during the time period of the show (W, G, or H), and finally, the total number of violent acts for that show's time period. Once again, look over the data collection sheet. Make sure you understand the procedure before you leave class today.

If your group wants to get a wide variety of data, discuss the shows you usually watch. If there is an overlap, maybe someone would be willing to watch another network and show. However, do not watch more TV than usual just for this assignment.

Step 2: Creating a Database and Entering the Data

When the week of data collection is over, review your data collection sheets. If more than one of you watched the same show, average the total scores for that show. Now enter the data into the database provided by your teacher. Make sure to enter the name of the show, the day of the week, and the time in the same format for easy entry. This will be very important when you sort the data by field type. Take turns entering the data. This can be a long and tedious process. If you share the work, it will go more quickly.

Step 3: Getting a Printout in List or Column Format

After all the data is entered, sort the records by the Day field. Once the database is sorted, your job is to print all the records in a list or column format. Try to make the information for each record fit on one line. In order to do this, you might have to adjust the page margins (try .5 inches first), and if that doesn't work, then change the size of the font to 10 or 8. If your program can display a print preview on the screen, use it before sending the report to the printer. Show your teacher a print preview before getting the printout. Include on the printout a title for the report and a list of names of all members in your group. Feel free to add additional labels, titles, or footers and headers that will improve the appearance of the printout. Some database programs even allow you to add graphics to the report.

Staple your data collection sheets to your printout and hand them in to your teacher.

In the next activity you will analyze your results.

16. Television Violence: Part II— Data Analysis

Skills: (1) **Database**—sorting records by field type and creating and printing reports, exporting a database report to a word processing file (optional). (2) **Word Processing**—starting a new document, editing, spell checking, saving and opening a file, and printing.

Objectives: To analyze data produced by a database. To generate reports sorted by specific fields. To work together in a group setting to draw conclusions about the data collected.

Level: Advanced.

Time Required: Two to three class periods.

Group Size: Three to six students.

Materials Needed: At least one computer per group with database and word processing software. Two computers would be ideal: one for studying database reports and the second for outlining the essay in a word processing document.

Procedure: Now that the data are entered into the database, students are ready to draw conclusions. Each group queries their database and comes up with facts that they write about in an essay and present to the class. Students can use a word processor to write the essay, and they can print their reports or export them into the word processing document.

Evaluation: Evaluate students based on group cooperation, group analysis of the data, the essay, and the presentation.

Special Tips: Students will need to know how to search a database with text and numeric queries.

Students will need to know how to generate reports in a list or column format. They should be able to add labels, footers, and headers and to print the reports to the screen as well as the printer. Make sure you see a print preview screen before each group prints, with a report in list or column format with labels including a title and the names of all group members. Many times, students use a format that prints each record on a separate sheet of paper. That's a lot of paper and a long bottleneck at the printer.

Discuss the accuracy of the data and the results of the survey. This truly isn't a foolproof way of collecting data, but it serves the purpose of making the students *aware* of TV violence. Also discuss the ill effects all this violence must be having on our society.

Combine all of the class groups' data, or even combine all of your classes' data. Have volunteers do the work and make final presentations to the classes.

Television Violence: Part II—Data Analysis

Analyzing data can be more fun than you think. Some of the conclusions you draw will be interesting and sometimes surprising. The key to analyzing data is to ask the database the right questions, or *queries*. Some of the possible queries you may consider are:

- How many acts of violence did you witness?

- What type of violence did you witness the most (G, W, H)?

- What type of violence did you witness the least (G, W, H)?

- Which network had the most violence?

- Which network had the least violence?

- What day of the week had the most violence?

It is your group's job to come up with other interesting queries. Take a closer look at the results and the categories themselves. What do you want to know? Can this database provide you with those answers?

Once you have made your queries and received the results, what conclusions can you draw about TV violence? For example, if you don't want to watch violence, when is the best time to watch TV and when is the worst time? As a group, write an essay stating some of the major conclusions you have drawn from your data.

The easiest way to find results for all your records is to generate reports sorting by specific fields. For example, sort by the Name of Show field so you can easily find the name of the show in your database. Or you can sort by the Total field in ascending or descending order to see which shows contain the most or least violence. Print out the reports or export them into your word processing document to justify your conclusions. Use the reports in your presentation, too.

Presenting your results to the class is always interesting. Some of the groups will draw the same conclusions, and some of the groups will differ greatly. Why is this? Is this a foolproof way of collecting information about TV violence? What about all the shows you didn't watch? In what ways could you conduct this study more accurately? Discuss these issues with your teacher and the rest of the class.

CHAPTER 3

Spreadsheet

17. Student Stockbrokers

Skills: (1) **Spreadsheet**—moving around the spreadsheet, entering text and numbers and simple formulas, and formatting cell contents (text: style, font type, size, justification, numbers: currency, number of decimal places; borders). (2) **Word Processing**—starting a new document, editing, spell checking, block operations, saving and opening a file, and printing.

Objectives: To use the imaginary buying and tracking of stock to familiarize students with the functions of a spreadsheet. To use small-group cooperative decision-making skills.

Level: Beginning.

Group Size: Three to six students.

Time Required: At least one week, but this is a wonderful activity to use throughout the quarter or semester. The main block of time is needed for creating the spreadsheet. Then give the selected group members 15 minutes at the beginning or end of Friday's class to enter the weekly stock quotes into the spreadsheet program. The actual retrieving of stock quotes could be a homework assignment. Students must come to class prepared, with the stock quotes in hand.

Materials Needed: One computer with spreadsheet capabilities per group. Access to stock quotes, through newspapers or on-line bulletin board services or the Internet.

Procedure: Students take on the roles of cooperative stockbrokers. As a group, they make decisions about purchasing five different company stocks. Each group then creates either one large spreadsheet or five individual spreadsheets. Students retrieve and enter stock quotes into the spreadsheet(s), calculating their daily profits or losses. Students track their stock purchases for as long as you want; this is a good extended-time activity. At the end of the activity, the groups print the spreadsheets with and without formulas. They also write and present reports to you and to the rest of the class.

Evaluation: Evaluate students based on small-group decision-making skills, the creation and use of the spreadsheet(s) and the group's presentation to the class.

Special Tips: Review the format for entering formulas with your spreadsheet program. The examples in this activity work with Microsoft Works and ClarisWorks.

This is a good activity to share with a math teacher.

Make sure group members take turns retrieving stock quotes and entering the quotes into the spreadsheet.

Check spreadsheets periodically to make sure all the formulas are correct.

Have the students compete against other classes. Which class can make the most money?

To save time, create the spreadsheet(s) for the groups and use the activity as data entry and analysis.

Student Stockbrokers

Imagine what it would be like to work on Wall Street as a stockbroker—all that yelling and screaming. There you are, selling hundreds of shares of IBM stock and the next moment buying thousands of shares of Microsoft stock. You look up from your computer to see a co-worker crying. He lost $2.5 million in the last trade. You feel sorry for him; but you're glad it's not you!

In this activity, you won't have to worry about losing real money. You and your group will be using your imaginations. After your teacher has divided you into groups, each team is assigned 5000 imaginary dollars. The object of this activity is for each group to create a *stock portfolio* (a collection of different company stocks) and try to make a profit. The group will keep track of profits and losses, purchases and sales through the use of a spreadsheet. Each group must select *five* company stocks to follow. You will follow these five stocks throughout the activity without any changes.

Once your group has decided on the company stocks, the next step is to create a spreadsheet to keep track of the daily profits or losses. The sample spreadsheet below displays two weeks of input for Intel stocks. You can make one large spreadsheet that tracks all five companies, or you can make five separate spreadsheets. If you make five separate spreadsheets, be sure to calculate by hand the amount of money you have left from the initial $5000.

Let's start by going over the formulas used and required in the spreadsheet in Figure 3.1.

	A	B	C	D
1	Initial Cash	$5000.00		
2				
3	Amount Left	$3760.00			= B1–B8 ①
4				
5	Name of Stock	Intel		
6	Price of Each Share	$62.00		
7	# of Shares Purchased	20		
8	Amount Invested	$1240.00			= B6*B7 ②
9				
10	Date	Posting	Value of All Shares	Profit/Loss
11	Monday (9/14)	60.75	$1215.00	-$25.00
12	Tuesday (9/15)	61.25	$1225.00	-$15.00
13	Wednesday (9/16)	63.00	$1260.00	$20.00
14	Thursday (9/17)	64.50	$1290.00	$50.00
15	Friday (9/18)	67.00	$1340.00	$100.00
16	Monday (9/21)	66.50	$1330.00	$90.00
17	Tuesday (9/22)	65.75	$1315.00	$75.00
18	Wednesday (9/23)	69.25	$1385.00	$145.00
19	Thursday (9/24)	70.00	$1400.00	$160.00
20	Friday (9/25)	68.25	$1365.00	$125.00

③ = C20–B8

④ = B20*B7

Figure 3.1

(continued)

Student Stockbrokers (continued)

Formula Descriptions

① This formula is located in cell B3 and keeps track of the amount of money you have left to invest.

② This formula is located in cell B8 and automatically calculates the amount spent on a stock. The result is found by multiplying the number of shares purchased by the price of the stock on the day the stock was purchased.

③ Every cell in the Profit/Loss column must have a formula similar to the one located here in cell D20. This formula calculates the profit or loss for the day by subtracting the amount you spent on the stock (cell B8) from the daily value of all of the stocks (cell C20).

④ Every cell in the Values of All Shares column must have a formula similar to the one located here in cell C20. The numbers are calculated automatically by multiplying the value in the Posting column (cell B20) by the number of shares purchased (cell B7).

Now, before making that first stock purchase, research potential profitable companies. Find those companies that you believe are going to make a profit in the near future. When a company does well, usually its stock prices go up. So which companies are doing well? Use your bulletin board service, the Internet, newspapers, and money magazines to do some investigating. Together, as a group, choose the companies you wish to invest in, and decide how much money you are going to spend on each company.

Every day, one of your group members should retrieve stock quotes from a bulletin board service, the Internet, or a newspaper. When your teacher allows you the time, enter the information into your spreadsheet(s).

At the end of the allotted time for this activity, your teacher will ask you to sell all your stock. Make a printout of your spreadsheet(s) that displays all the entries and another printout that displays all the formulas used. From the printout containing the number results, use a word processing program to write a short report about your portfolio. Some of the questions you need to answer are:

1. How much money did you make or lose on the whole portfolio?
2. Which stock did the best?
3. Which stock did the worst?
4. Which stock jumped around the most?
5. What was your best group-buying decision?
6. What was your worst group-buying decision?

Present your report to the rest of the class, and hand in the written report and spreadsheet printouts to your teacher. After all the groups have given their reports, identify which group made the most money.

18. Squeezing Money out of a Lemon—Part I: The Spreadsheet

Skills: (1) **Spreadsheet**—moving around the spreadsheet, entering text and numbers and simple formulas, and formatting cell contents (text: style, font type, size, justification; numbers: currency, number of decimal places; borders). (2) **Word Processing**—starting a new document, editing, spell checking, block operations, saving and opening a file, and printing.

Objectives: To use a spreadsheet to determine the possible profitability of an imaginary lemonade stand. To use small-group cooperative learning decision-making skills.

Level: Intermediate.

Group Size: Three to six students.

Time Required: One class period if students are loading the spreadsheet file created by the teacher. Two class periods if students are required to enter the spreadsheet.

Materials Needed: One computer per group with spreadsheet and word processing capabilities.

Procedure: Often students want to know "What's in it for me?" before they put forth an effort. For those kinds of students, this is a perfect activity. Students use a preexisting spreadsheet program to predict future profitability of an imaginary lemonade stand. The spreadsheet format is shown with and without formulas in the student section. Either the students or you can enter the spreadsheet. Students then play with the numbers in order to determine the best plan of action for selling lemonade. Each group writes a report and presents their numbers and ideas to you and the rest of the class.

Evaluation: Evaluate students based on spreadsheet use and small-group interaction. Students are also evaluated based on the final report and presentation.

Special Tips: Review the format for entering formulas with your spreadsheet program. The examples in this activity work with Microsoft Works and ClarisWorks.

This is a good activity to share with a home and career teacher.

The item the students sell does not have to be lemonade. Let the students choose what they wish to sell.

For a challenge, have students add the month of **September** to the bottom and top of the spreadsheet. The Total information at the top of the spreadsheet will have to be moved to column F to make room for September statistics.

Squeezing Money out of a Lemon—Part I: The Spreadsheet

Just imagine that during the upcoming summer, you and your group have decided to earn some money. The meteorologists have predicted a long, hot summer. So a lemonade stand should be a perfect moneymaking idea. But how do you know it will be successful? Will it be profitable? How much money will it cost to get started? Is it going to be worth the effort?

You can answer all of these questions through the use of a spreadsheet. The spreadsheet shown in Figure 3.2 keeps track of the profits and expenses of your imaginary lemonade stand. Using a spreadsheet will help your group determine the price to charge for a glass of lemonade in order to optimize your profits. Look over the spreadsheet, and then check out the spreadsheet in Figure 3.3. It displays all the formulas needed to make this lemonade spreadsheet work.

	A	B	C	D	E	F
1	Sean's Lemonade Stand					
2						
3		June	July	August	Total	
4	Sales	$40.00	$125.00	$240.00	$405.00	
5	Expenses	$20.00	$50.00	$120.00	$190.00	
6	Profit	$20.00	$75.00	$120.00	$215.00	
7						
8	June Sales and Expenses					
9	Ingredients	Cost/Cup	Cost Totals		# Sold	100
10	Lemons	$0.10	$10.00		Price/Cup	$0.40
11	Sugar	$0.02	$2.00		Total Sales	$40.00
12	Cups	$0.03	$3.00			
13	Ads		$5.00			
14	Total Expenses		$20.00			
15						
16	July Sales and Expenses					
17	Ingredients	Cost/Cup	Cost Totals		# Sold	250
18	Lemons	$0.10	$25.00		Price/Cup	$0.50
19	Sugar	$0.02	$5.00		Total Sales	$125.00
20	Cups	$0.03	$7.50			
21	Ads		$12.50			
22	Total Expenses		$50.00			
23						
24	August Sales and Expenses					
25	Ingredients	Cost/Cup	Cost Totals		# Sold	400
26	Lemons	$0.20	$80.00		Price/Cup	$0.60
27	Sugar	$0.02	$8.00		Total Sales	$240.00
28	Cups	$0.03	$12.00			
29	Ads		$20.00			
30	Total Expenses		$120.00			
31						
32						

Figure 3.2

(continued)

Squeezing Money out of a Lemon—
Part I: The Spreadsheet *(continued)*

	A	B	C	D	E	F
1	Sean's Lemonade Stand					
2						
3		June	July	August	Total	
4	Sales	=F11	=F19	=F27	=SUM(B4..D4)	
5	Expenses	=C14	=C22	=C30	=SUM(B5..D5)	
6	Profit	=B4-B5	=C4-C5	=D4-D5	=E4-E5	
7						
8	June Sales and Expenses					
9	Ingredients	Cost/Cup	Cost Totals		# Sold	100
10	Lemons	$0.10	=B10*F9		Price/Cup	$0.40
11	Sugar	$0.02	=B11*F9		Total Sales	=F9*F10
12	Cups	$0.03	=B12*F9			
13	Ads		$5.00			
14	Total Expenses		=SUM(C10..C13)			
15						
16	July Sales and Expenses					
17	Ingredients	Cost/Cup	Cost Totals		# Sold	250
18	Lemons	$0.10	=B18*F17		Price/Cup	$0.50
19	Sugar	$0.02	=B19*F17		Total Sales	=F17*F18
20	Cups	$0.03	=B20*F17			
21	Ads		$12.50			
22	Total Expenses		=SUM(C18..C21)			
23						
24	August Sales and Expenses					
25	Ingredients	Cost/Cup	Cost Totals		# Sold	400
26	Lemons	$0.20	=B26*F25		Price/Cup	$0.60
27	Sugar	$0.02	=B27*F25		Total Sales	=F25*F26
28	Cups	$0.03	=B28*F25			
29	Ads		$20.00			
30	Total Expenses		=SUM(C26..C29)			
31						
32						

Figure 3.3

In this activity, your group is responsible for entering the correct information into the spreadsheet and then experimenting with the spreadsheet to predict a few different outcomes. Try entering a new number for the cost of lemons or sugar and watch how it affects the spreadsheet. Change the number of cups sold to a low number and see what happens. Experiment with the numbers. By trying different scenarios, you can determine the best course of action for the summer sales. Keep in mind that you must keep your prices reasonable, or no one will buy your lemonade.

When your group has come up with what you believe to be the best possible scenario, print two copies of your spreadsheet, one displaying formulas and one without the formulas. Include a short report explaining your decisions. Also in the report, include any ideas on advertising, lemonade stand location, possible franchises, or other ideas that might increase your profits. Present your report to the teacher and to the rest of the class.

19. Squeezing Money out of a Lemon— Part II: The Charts

Skills: **Spreadsheet**—creating a bar and pie chart and printing a chart.

Objectives: To create bar and pie charts through the use of a spreadsheet program. To use small-group interaction to create charts.

Level: Intermediate.

Time Required: Two class periods.

Group Size: Three to six students.

Materials Needed: At least one computer with spreadsheet capabilities per group. A color printer would be nice but is not required. Students can color their charts with conventional utensils after the charts have been printed.

Demonstrations Needed: Show students how a chart is created. They will need to know how to modify an existing chart. Add as many features to the chart as possible.

Procedure: This activity is designed to motivate students to use the chart-making feature of the lemonade spreadsheet in Activity 18. Chart making is an important step to do and understand. Each group reproduces three charts displayed on the student handout and creates one additional chart of their choice. Students are free to add color, patterns, and other attributes to their charts. Students print each chart and hand it in for evaluation. Display some of the charts with unique characteristics for other students to see.

Evaluation: Evaluate students based on group interaction and the final charts.

Special Tips: The charts displayed in the student sections were created in ClarisWorks. ClarisWorks does allow a chart to be displayed on the same screen as the spreadsheet. Not all spreadsheets will allow you do this. Also, graphics or drawings can be added to a ClarisWorks chart.

See if your word processor will import a chart created in your spreadsheet. If so and if you have the time, have students import their charts into a word processing document. In the word processing document, have students explain the meaning of each chart.

Name _____ Date _____

Squeezing Money out of a Lemon—Part II: The Charts

Creating a visual representation of spreadsheet data is one of the most powerful tools a business entrepreneur can use. You can look at and understand charts very quickly. You don't have to page through columns of data to understand the big picture. A chart can do the work for you. What's fascinating is that when you change numbers in the spreadsheet, the chart changes accordingly, right before your eyes.

In this activity, you and your lemonade stand group are going to create four charts. These charts will represent information from your lemonade spreadsheet. Using the lemonade spreadsheet, create three charts very similar to those shown below. Once you have a basic chart created, feel free to experiment with color, patterns, and other attributes to make your chart more visually appealing. The fourth chart can represent whatever your group decides to visualize.

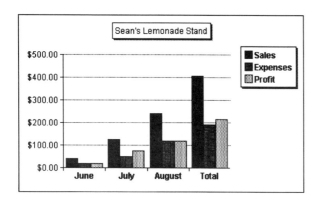

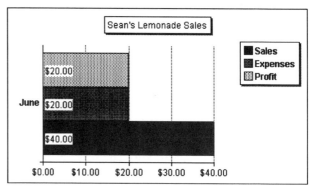

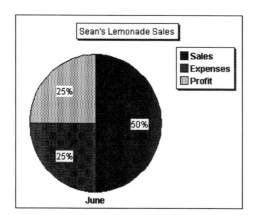

When you have finished your charts, print them and hand them in to your teacher for evaluation. Your teacher will display some of the charts. Check to see what other groups designed.

         61 Cooperative Learning Activities for Computer Classrooms

20. Brownie Entrepreneurs

Skills: **Spreadsheet**—moving around the spreadsheet, entering text and numbers and simple formulas, and formatting cell contents (text: style, font type, size, justification; numbers: currency, number of decimal places; borders).

Objectives: To have the students create their own spreadsheet using a brownie-selling scenario. To use small-group interaction to answer questions about the created spreadsheet.

Level: Advanced.

Time Required: Two to three class periods.

Group Size: Three to six students.

Materials Needed: One computer per group with spreadsheet capabilities and a printer.

Demonstration Needed: Complete the spreadsheet and demonstrate how it works. During the demonstration, discuss a few of the formulas.

Procedure: Now your students will have the chance to sell brownies and use a spreadsheet to calculate profits. This activity requires each group of students to create a spreadsheet that will generate statistical information from a list of brownie ingredients. Given the brownie ingredient list and the total number of brownies per batch and how much to charge for a brownie, students can determine

such things as: the total cost per batch, cost per brownie, cost per a given number of batches, total expenses, and total profits. Each group must figure out all the formulas in the spreadsheet. Once the spreadsheet is working correctly, students are required to print out the spreadsheet with and without the formulas. They must also solve two additional problems, using the working spreadsheet.

Evaluation: Evaluate students based on small-group interaction, the spreadsheet they create (including the printouts), and the answers to the summary questions.

Special Tips: Answers to activity-ending questions: (1) $46.72   (2) $9.12

Work with the math teacher to come up with additional word problems for the spreadsheet that the students can use in the math classroom.

Create more questions for students to solve, or have students write at least five problems for other groups to solve. Students can enter these problems into a word processing document. Have the students print the problems and the answers and hand them in to you.

Have students update the spreadsheet to work with another recipe. How about chocolate chip cookies?

Name _____   Date _____

Brownie Entrepreneurs

In this activity, you and your group pretend to sell brownies in order to raise money for new computers and software. You keep track of your expenses, sales, and profits by using a spreadsheet. However, you create your own spreadsheet. Your goal in this activity is to create a spreadsheet that looks similar to the one shown in Figure 3.4. It includes a list of the brownie ingredients along with all the statistics displayed below. Once the spreadsheet is working correctly, you will be asked to use it to solve a few problems. So look over the directions, and get cooking!

	A	B	C	D	E
1	Your Name			Date	
2	Class			Teacher	
3					
4	Brownie Recipe				
5		Amount			
6	Ingredients	Needed		Cost	Totals
7	Unsweetened Chocolate	4 ounces		$0.20	$0.80
8	Shortening	0.5 cup		$0.20	$0.10
9	Sugar	2 cups		$0.15	$0.30
10	Eggs	4 eggs		$0.08	$0.32
11	Flour	1 cup		$0.04	$0.04
12	Baking Powder	1 teaspoon		$0.04	$0.04
13	Salt	1 teaspoon		$0.01	$0.01
14	Chopped Nuts	1 cup		$0.55	$0.55
15					
16					
17	Yield	32 brownies			
18					
19	Total Cost per Batch	$2.16			
20	Cost per Brownie	$0.07			
21					
22	# of Batches	5	10	20	50
23	# of Brownies	160	320	640	1600
24					
25	Amount Charged	$0.25			
26	Total Collected	$40.00	$80.00	$160.00	$400.00
27	Total Expenses	$10.80	$21.60	$43.20	$108.00
28					
29	Total Profits	$29.20	$58.40	$116.80	$292.00

Figure 3.4

Directions:

Start by creating a new spreadsheet file, and save it under the name **BROWNIES**. The next step is to enter all text and numeric data that do not require any formulas. Make sure your spreadsheet contains all the information shown in Figure 3.5. Now for the hard part. All of the remaining cells of the spreadsheet in Figure 3.4 that contain numeric information must contain formulas that automatically update results when new numbers are entered into cells of the spreadsheet in Figure 3.5 that contain numbers. As a group, you must determine what all of the formulas are. You know the formulas are correct if they generate the same answers shown in Figure 3.4.

(continued)

Name _____ Date _____

Brownie Entrepreneurs *(continued)*

Finally, print a copy of the spreadsheet with and without the formulas. Once the spreadsheet is completed, use it to solve the following problems. Write the answers on a piece of paper, and hand in the paper and both printouts to your teacher.

1. How much profit will you make selling 8 batches of brownies?

2. You plan to sell 12 batches of brownies. Unfortunately, the cost of unsweetened chocolate is 35 cents and the cost of an egg is up to 12 cents. How much profit will you lose by purchasing the unsweetened chocolate and eggs at the given prices?

	A	B	C	D	E
1	Your Name			Date	
2	Class			Teacher	
3					
4	Brownie Recipe				
5		Amount			
6	Ingredients	Needed		Cost	Totals
7	Unsweetened Chocolate	4 ounces		$0.20	
8	Shortening	0.5 cup		$0.20	
9	Sugar	2 cups		$0.15	
10	Eggs	4 eggs		$0.08	
11	Flour	1 cup		$0.04	
12	Baking Powder	1 teaspoon		$0.04	
13	Salt	1 teaspoon		$0.01	
14	Chopped Nuts	1 cup		$0.55	
15					
16					
17	Yield	32 brownies			
18					
19	Total Cost per Batch				
20	Cost per Brownie				
21					
22	# of Batches	5	10	20	50
23	# of Brownies				
24					
25	Amount Charged	$0.25			
26	Total Collected				
27	Total Expenses				
28					
29	Total Profits				

Figure 3.5

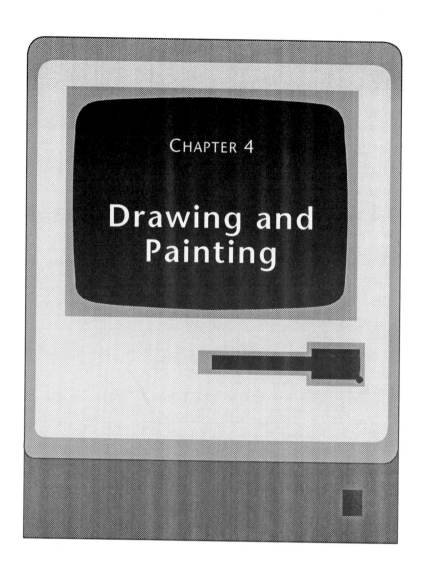

CHAPTER 4

Drawing and Painting

21. Cubism

Skills: **Drawing/Painting**—Painting tools include: line, spray paint, polygon, box, rounded box, ellipse, curve, and fill. Editing tools include: eraser, color eraser, and the undo command. Block operations include: copy, move, shrink and grow, tilt, flip, rotate, and inverse.

Objectives: To create a piece of cubist art using only one main drawing tool and small-group interaction.

Level: Beginning.

Time Required: One class period.

Group Size: Three to six students.

Materials Needed: One computer with draw/paint software per group. A large-screen monitor could be used to display the project while each group makes their presentation to the class.

Demonstrations Needed: Because students have a difficult time understanding cubism, you may want to show them a few examples. To find examples, research in an encyclopedia, CD-ROM encyclopedia, and/or art books, or contact your school's art teacher. If all else fails, try the activity yourself. Students love to see what teachers can do. Present a hard-copy example or download an example onto students' computers or a large-screen monitor. Go over all the tools and features needed to complete the assignment. Review the undo command as well as how to copy, shrink, enlarge, tilt, flip, and rotate an object.

Procedure: Each group creates a work of art in the cubist style using only one assigned drawing/painting tool. Each group member spends time working on the design. Students are allowed to copy, shrink, enlarge, tilt, flip, and rotate sections of their work but cannot use any drawing/painting tool other than the one assigned to them. When the design is nearly completed, students can use the fill tool to add color or patterns. Each group presents their completed project to the class, whether on a large-screen monitor or by having group members circulate around the room. One member of each group describes the process used to create their cubist work.

Evaluation: Evaluate students based on group interaction and the final group product.

Special Tips: Allow students to use the fill tool only after they have created a basic design. Students often are distracted by the fill tool and lose the sense of the design's basic composition.

Upon completion of the activity, save the students' work to one of your disks. Print a few of the cubist artworks and display them on a bulletin board, or create a self-running slide show for current or future classes to see.

If this activity is a success in your classroom, extend it by simply having each group try a new tool. Next time, limit the students to two tools. Finally, allow the students to use all of the tools.

Find an example of a famous piece of cubist art. Ask the students to create their own artwork emulating that particular style. Emphasize that they are not to copy the painting itself.

Cubism

In this activity, you are going to create a work of art in the *cubist* style. What is *cubism*? It is a form of modern art using abstract geometric forms rather than lifelike representation of the real world. In other words, cubist art doesn't "look like" anything.

How do you go about creating cubist art? Just follow these steps:

1. Your teacher will divide your class into groups and assign your group to a computer.

2. Load your drawing or painting program. Now your teacher will assign your group one drawing tool. This is the only drawing tool you will be allowed to use. You may copy, move, shrink, enlarge, tilt, flip, rotate, and inverse any section of the picture, and of course you can use the undo command to wipe out any mistakes.

3. Begin drawing. Take turns using the tool. Remember, your artwork isn't supposed to "look like" anything. Simply make designs. Do not criticize fellow group members for their additions to the artwork. There is no right or wrong way. You may not like a person's addition, but this is a group project in which everyone has a chance to contribute.

4. After you have finished the basic drawing, every group member needs to take a turn adding color to the project by using the fill tool.

5. Upon completion of your project, display a full screen preview of your cubist work.

6. Present your cubist art to the rest of the class. A representative of your group should explain which drawing tool you used in your artwork, along with your group's approach to the project. If time allows, try this activity again as a group. But this time use a different drawing tool.

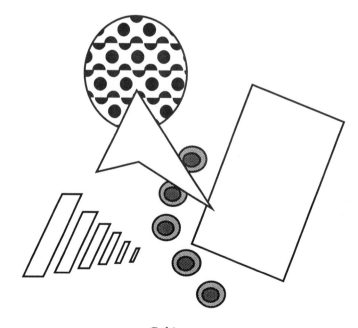

Cubism

22. Face It

Skills: (1) **Drawing/Painting**—Painting tools include: line, spray paint, polygon, box, rounded box, ellipse, curve, and fill. Editing tools include: zoom, eraser, color eraser, and the undo command. Block operations include: copy, move, shrink and grow, tilt, flip, rotate, and inverse.
(2) **Word Processing**—starting a new document, editing, spell checking, saving and opening a file, and printing.

Objectives: To create art using as many drawing/painting tools as possible. To use small-group cooperation.

Level: Intermediate.

Time Required: One class period.

Group Size: Three to five students.

Materials Needed: Two computers per group, drawing/painting software, word processing software, and a printer.

Demonstration Needed: You may need to review a few of the drawing/painting tools to help the students get started.

Procedure: Students love to draw pictures of faces, and they get the opportunity to do just that in this activity. Each group is required to use as many drawing/painting tools as possible while creating a picture of a face. They log the different types of tools used and which feature each tool was used to create, along with any special effects added to the design (copy, flip, rotate, inverse, etc.). Students create the log by hand or on a word processing document on an adjacent computer. Each group presents their completed project to the class, displaying their face on a large-screen monitor or having group members circulate around the room. One member of each group describes the process taken to complete the assignment. The group that used the most drawing/painting tools in the allotted time wins.

Evaluation: Evaluate students based on group interaction, the number of tools used, and the end product.

Special Tips: Watch the clock. You will want to leave enough time for the presentations. To save time, eliminate the tool list requirement.

If you have a large-screen monitor, have some of the students demonstrate the tools they used in front of the class. This takes time; you may want to do it the next day.

Upon completion of the activity, save the students' work to one of your disks. Print a few and display them on a bulletin board, or create a self-running slide show for current or future classes to see.

Instead of a face, have the students draw an object they are studying in another class such as an insect, the Liberty Bell, or a flag.

Name _____   Date _____

Face It

Here's a quick drawing activity that can bring fascinating fun and a lot of laughs. After your teacher has placed you in a group, sit together at two computers. Make sure your drawing/painting software is up and running on one computer, with your word processing software running on the other.

The object of this activity is to draw a face, using as many drawing and painting tools as possible. Each group member takes a turn drawing a facial feature with a different tool. Record each tool you use, and what feature you created with it, in a new word processing document. If this is not possible, simply write the list on a piece of notebook paper. Also, log names of all members of the group and the variety of special-effect tools used such as: copy, move, shrink and grow, tilt, flip, rotate, and inverse.

Keep in mind that you are competing against the rest of the groups in your class. The team that successfully uses the greatest number of drawing and painting tools at the end of the allotted time wins!

When your teacher announces, "Time's up," stop drawing and make sure your list is complete. Print the word processing document, and display a full-screen preview of the picture of the face. As a group, present your picture to the class. Explain all the tools you used to create the face. Be prepared to demonstrate the procedures you used. Your teacher may call on you to demonstrate a tool.

After all the presentations, give your printout log to the teacher. Your teacher will announce the winning team. Just for fun, take a vote on the pictures themselves. Which picture do you like best? Which picture does the class like the best? Ask your teacher to print some or all of the pictures and display them somewhere special.

23. Frame by Frame: Part I

Skills: (1) **Drawing/Painting**—Painting tools include: line, spray paint, polygon, box, rounded box, ellipse, curve, and fill. Editing tools include: zoom, eraser, color eraser, and the undo command. Block operations include: copy, move, shrink and grow, tilt, flip, rotate, and inverse. (2) **Word Processing**—starting a new document, editing, spell checking, saving and opening a file, and printing.

Objectives: To create a comic strip through the use of computer drawing/painting skills and small group interaction.

Level: Advanced.

Time Required: Three class periods.

Group Size: Three to six students.

Materials Needed: One computer per group, drawing/painting software, word processing software, and a printer. If your resources are limited, this exercise could partially or completely be done with pen and paper. If you do not have a color printer, simply have the students print a black-and-white version of the comic strip, then color it in using colored pencils or markers.

Demonstrations Needed: You may need to demonstrate to the students how to get started. This is usually the hardest part. If at all possible, use a big-screen monitor. Show the students comic strips you have made or examples of other students' work.

Procedure: Students have the challenge of creating their very own comic strip, from the initial brainstorming to the actual painting of each frame. Each member of the group is responsible for one frame of the strip. While only one computer is needed to complete the story outline, it would be helpful for each member of the group to have her or his own computer during the painting process. The activity concludes with a group presentation to the class.

Evaluation: Evaluate students based on group cooperation and the final product.

Special Tips: Encourage the students to create a comic strip with dialogue.

Emphasize the use of note taking while students are brainstorming. Explain the importance of a story line. Most students are familiar with the term *outline*. Explain that a story line and an outline serve the same purpose—to help organize, to have a plan. Collect a printout of each outline so you can see the direction each group is taking with the project.

If a group uses a particularly interesting technique, you may want them to present it to the rest of the class.

This presents an excellent cooperative teaching opportunity with your art teacher.

Name _____ Date _____

Frame by Frame: Part I

Students often think the most interesting section in a newspaper is the funnies or comic strip page, and some adults feel that way, too. In this activity, you will have the chance to create your own comic strip with the help of a few friends and a computer.

After your teacher has divided you into groups, take time to talk about possible comic strip ideas. As a group, you need to make a few key decisions. What kind of comic strip do you want to create? a funny comic strip? superhero? political? mystery? Is your comic strip going to have any dialogue, or is it going to be pictures only?

Once you've chosen the type of comic strip, you need to brainstorm (share ideas) about a story line. Are your characters going to tell a joke, be in an adventure, make a political statement? Take notes in a word processing document so you don't forget any great ideas.

Next, each group member needs an assignment. Each member could be responsible for one *frame* or box of the comic strip. This doesn't mean you can't help each other. In fact, you have to work together for the sake of story line and organization.

Now start drawing. Use the draw/paint software you are familiar with. Sit together at one computer until everyone is familiar with the "look" of the characters. One team member does the drawing, while the other group members make verbal contributions. You may want to make a quick sketch of the whole comic strip so everyone has an idea of what they need to do. Continue to work at one computer, or take your individual assignments and work on your own.

Make sure to share drawing and painting hints and suggestions with each other. Some group members may not know how to use the drawing or painting tools you know how to use. Remember, you will be graded not only on your individual frame but also on the comic strip as a whole. Helping one another is the key to success on this project.

After you have finished drawing, print your individual frames. If you do not have a colored printer, simply add color to your comic strip by using colored pencils, crayons, or markers. Now place the frames next to each other and in order, creating a true comic "strip." You may want to mount your comic strip on tag board or construction paper. Your teacher may provide a bulletin board or wall space to display your group's fine artwork.

Take time to admire other groups' comic strips. Note the tools they used. Maybe next time you can use some of their clever ideas.

24. Frame by Frame: Part II

Skills: (1) **Drawing/Painting**—Painting tools include: line, spray paint, polygon, box, rounded box, ellipse, curve, and fill. Editing tools include: zoom, eraser, color eraser, and the undo command. Block operations include: copy, move, shrink and grow, tilt, flip, rotate, and inverse.
(2) **Word Processing**—starting a new document, editing, spell checking, saving and opening a file, and printing.

Objectives: To create a comic book through the use of computer drawing/painting skills and small group interaction.

Level: Advanced.

Time Required: Progressive project.

Group Size: Three to six students.

Materials Needed: One computer per group, drawing/painting software, word processing software, and a printer. If your resources are limited, this could partially or completely be done with pen and paper. If you do not have a color printer, simply have the students print a black-and-white version of the comic strip, then color it in using colored pencils or markers.

Demonstration Needed: If you have not completed the previous activity, you may need to demonstrate the techniques used to create a basic five- or six-frame comic strip.

Procedure: Students create an entire comic book. You can have each group complete the project or have the whole class tackle it. Either way, your students will enjoy the challenge of planning out a story line and following through with the painted frames. This project can take place over a set of days or be broken up throughout the quarter. Presentation of all comic books is a must for all classes at any grade level.

Evaluation: Evaluate students based on group interaction and the final product. Student progress reports will also factor into the final grade.

Special Tips: The length of the comic book depends on your requirements and your curriculum. The recommended time segment is one frame per week per student.

To keep this progressive project on track, periodically have students take 10 minutes at the end of a class to type a summary of their group's progress. Read the printout and feel free to view the progress.

When the final projects are due, declare it Comic Book Day! Have the students present their comic books. Allow the rest of the class period for exchange of projects, as well as the exchange of comic books the students have brought from home.

Start a comic book club. Interested students could create their own characters and stories, or they could try to emulate their favorite comic book style. You'll be surprised how proficient students become with drawing/painting software when they are creating something they enjoy.

Name _____ Date _____

Frame by Frame: Part II

After completing "Frame by Frame: Part I," you have a pretty good idea of what's involved in creating a comic strip. Now you are going to take it one step further. Your group or class is going to create a complete comic book! Don't worry; you don't have to create the whole thing in two days. This is a progressive project, which means your group will work on it a little at a time.

Your group can use the character and story line you created in the first activity, or you can start all over. Basically, follow the same steps laid out in the first activity. Here is a quick reminder:

1. Brainstorm for ideas about character and story line.

2. Take notes, preferably on a word processor.

3. Use the drawing/painting software to create the individual frames.

4. Add text and color.

Throughout the project, your teacher will be checking up on your group. Occasionally, you will be required to type a progress report to hand in to your teacher. Be prepared to display your progress to your teacher at any time. So make sure your progress reports are detailed and accurate. Keep up with the project, and try not to save too much work for the final days.

When your teacher announces the date the final project is due, your group needs to start thinking about the comic book cover. This is a very important aspect of the project. Not only is it the largest piece of artwork, it is the first piece of artwork your teacher and others will see. As a group, put some special effort into the cover.

On the day your projects are due, you will present your comic book to the class. A representative from your group should tell a little about the story line and the drawing/painting techniques your group used. Pass the book around the class for everyone to see. Finally, give the book to your teacher to grade.

25. Coat of Arms

Skills: **Drawing/Painting**—Painting tools include: line, spray paint, polygon, box, rounded box, ellipse, curve, and fill. Editing tools include: zoom, eraser, color eraser, and the undo command. Block operations include: copy, move, shrink and grow, tilt, flip, rotate, and inverse.

Objectives: To create an art project through the use of drawing/painting software and cooperative learning.

Level: Advanced.

Time Required: Two class periods.

Group Size: Three to five students.

Materials Needed: One computer per group and drawing/painting software. If your resources are limited, this exercise could partially or completely be done with pen and paper. If you have access to more than one computer per group—great! Students can use their own computer to sketch out their individual symbols. A printer is not a requirement, but it would be nice for students to print and display their coats of arms.

Demonstration Needed: Try to find examples of different types of coats of arms for the students to look at and emulate. If you have a big-screen monitor, display a coat of arms from a CD-ROM encyclopedia and leave it there as a reference.

Procedure: Each group creates a coat of arms that symbolizes the group. In addition, each group member creates a symbol that represents himself or herself as an individual. A group motto is also required. Students use drawing/painting software. Each group will present their completed project to the class.

Evaluation: Evaluate students based on group participation, individual symbols, the final product, and presentation.

Special Tips: For research, try to have a printed or CD-ROM encyclopedia in the classroom. Check to make sure your CD-ROM program actually has sample pictures of coats of arms.

Review drawing/painting tools that you feel would be helpful. But this activity is for advanced students, who should have previous drawing/painting experience.

Try creating a class coat of arms. Take suggestions on the class symbol or mascot, and don't forget to come up with a class motto. The class can take a vote on the items. Have volunteers create the coat of arms during free time.

Having individual students create their own coat of arms would be an excellent project for extra credit.

Name _____ Date _____

Coat of Arms

What is a *coat of arms*? In England, around the fourteenth century, a knight would wear an emblem or decoration over his armor. Because a knight's armor covered him so completely, this emblem was necessary for identification. A friend or an enemy could recognize him by the colors and symbols on his coat of arms. These colors and symbols usually represented his family and home.

Today you are going to create a coat of arms. But first you must form a family. After your teacher has divided you into groups or families, look at some coats of arms in your CD-ROM or printed encyclopedia.

Now that you know what a coat of arms looks like, work with your group members to create a coat of arms that represents you as a group. Make the coat of arms in any style you wish, but make sure it meets the following requirements:

1. All artwork must be done with drawing/painting software (your teacher may make exceptions). Work together sharing information about different drawing/painting tools.

2. Each group member must be represented on the coat of arms by his or her own individual symbol. Each group member is responsible for designing and drawing his or her symbol.

3. The coat of arms must also have one symbol to represent the group as a whole. Discuss possible ideas. If necessary, take a vote on which idea your group likes the best.

4. The coat of arms must have a motto. A motto is a word, phrase, or sentence describing, referring to, or representing the group or family. Once again, as a group, discuss the possible ideas for a motto. If need be, take a vote.

Once you have all the ideas gathered together, start drawing. As an individual, you may wish to make a rough sketch of your symbol before using the computer.

When you have finished your group coat of arms, present it to the rest of the class. You are responsible for explaining why the symbol you chose represents you. A group representative can explain the group symbol and motto.

26. Technology Collage

Skills: **Drawing/Painting**—Painting tools include: line, spray paint, polygon, box, rounded box, ellipse, curve, and fill. Editing tools include: zoom, eraser, color eraser, and the undo command. Block operations include: copy, move, shrink and grow, tilt, flip, rotate, and inverse.

Objectives: To use draw/paint software and small-group cooperation to create a collage.

Level: Intermediate.

Time Required: Two class periods.

Group Size: Three to eight students.

Materials Needed: Computer magazines, one computer with draw/paint software per student, printer, construction paper or tag board, scissors, glue, and colored writing utensils.

Procedure: A great way to introduce the variety of computer hardware parts on the market today is to have students create a collage of as many different computer components as possible. Each group member is responsible for drawing a different part of the collage. Groups put their collages together when all individual drawings are completed and present them to the class.

Evaluation: Evaluate students based on group interaction, individual contribution, and final group project.

Special Tips: Constantly remind students that the object they choose to draw must somehow be related to computer technology.

Remind students that their drawings do not have to be perfect. A close rendering is fine.

Designate a section of your room, away from the computer, for the actual construction of the collages. Glue near computers is not advisable.

You can have individuals create their own collage or have the whole class create one collage.

A nice way to display your students' work is to create a collage of all of the group collages.

Require groups to define as many components in the collage as possible. During the presentation, you or other students can ask each group to define specific hardware pieces displayed in the collage.

Name _____ Date _____

Technology Collage

In this activity, you and your group are going to create a collage of technology. After your teacher has divided you into groups, follow these steps:

1. As an individual, choose a piece of computer technology you wish to draw. Maybe you would like to draw a mouse, keyboard, monitor, disk, disk drive, CD-ROM drive, or even the computer you are using. Page through a computer magazine to get some ideas. The more unusual the item you choose, the more interesting your drawing and group collage will be. In addition, no one in the same group is allowed to draw the same item. Just remember, it must have something to do with computer technology.

2. After you have chosen a subject, use your drawing/painting software to create a realistic picture of your subject.

3. As a group, share ideas and drawing/painting techniques. Help each other out.

4. When you have finished your drawing, print it.

5. As a group, create a collage with all your pictures. Feel free to cut your pictures out. Paste your pictures to a piece of construction paper or tag board. If you didn't print your drawings with a color printer, simply add color by using crayons, markers, or colored pencils.

6. Vote on a name for your group collage.

7. Present your collage to the class.

CHAPTER 5

Desktop
Publishing

27. Ads for Sea Monkeys

Skills: **Desktop Publishing**—entering text or importing a text document into a text frame, changing text (style, size, font type, alignment, and spacing), moving a text frame, importing and customizing graphics (resize, flip, move, copy), selecting a page layout, and saving and printing a document.

Objectives: To become familiar with and use desktop publishing or stationery software. To use small-group cooperative learning to create magazine classified ads.

Level: Beginning.

Time Required: Two class periods.

Group Size: Three to six students.

Materials Needed: One computer per group with desktop publishing capabilities and clip art. A color printer if possible; if not, students will need conventional coloring utensils. Appropriate teen magazine or comic book classified ads.

Procedure: Students enjoy this activity because they are allowed to use their creative juices in a silly way. Each group writes and lays out five magazine classified ads using a desktop publishing or stationery program. Writing magazine classified ads is fun because the ads themselves are so outlandish. Students can stretch their imaginations without fear of being ridiculed. In addition, most students enjoy using desktop publishing or stationery software because of the ease with which graphics and fancy fonts can be manipulated. This activity is designed to help beginning students become familiar with the software through the use of small group interaction and creative writing. After the groups have written their five ads, print and display the ads for all your students to read.

Evaluation: Evaluate students based on small group interaction, use of desktop publishing or stationery software, and the final product.

Special Tips: The ads are meant to be silly or outlandish. Let the students go wild with this activity, but make sure they keep the material appropriate. Be sure sample ads your students bring in are appropriate, too.

A stationery program is recommended for younger students. A card layout allows creation of two ads: one on the card's front and one on the inside. Older students can use a desktop publishing program that can import graphics and text. These students can type their ads in a word processing document, spell check, and save it in a format (ASCII) that your desktop publishing program recognizes.

Have the groups combine their ads into one large classified ad section. Students could go on to put together an entire magazine, with articles about each other and the latest in computer technology, plus examples of their work.

Ads for Sea Monkeys

Have you ever looked at the classified ad section in the back of a magazine or comic book? The pages are usually filled to the edges with silly or unusual ads. For example, some of them may look like this:

Parent Control: Are your parents out of control? Do they live to tell you to clean your room and even do your homework? Well, here is the answer to your problem:

The Atomic Parent-Reversal Remote Control

Just use this handy, dandy box to reverse the decision of even the most demanding parent. Press a button, and all of a sudden your parents are cleaning your room and doing all your homework. How can you go wrong? Box comes with manual and a money-back guarantee.

Call 1-800-PARENTS for Latest Price

Sea Monkeys

The real live thing!
All you have to do is add water,
and the sea monkeys will come to life.
Watch them swim around
and change colors.
These wonderful pets can be yours for

 $19.95

Call 1-800-MONKEYS
for your monkeys NOW!
(Add 1.50 for shipping and handling.)

Magazine classified ads are fun to read and fun to write. As a small group, you will be responsible for writing five ads. After your teacher has divided you into groups, start brainstorming for possible ad ideas. Take a look at the back of teen magazines and comic books. *Do not copy*, but you can use an idea or two. Also note what these ads look like. They are small, appear in boxes, and some have graphics.

Once your group has come up with a list of ideas, start writing. Use your desktop publishing software to give your writing the appearance of a real ad. Add graphics and fancy fonts.

Add color to the graphics by using a color printer or by using conventional coloring utensils. Print your ads for your teacher to look at and grade. In the end, post your ads on the bulletin board for everyone to read and enjoy.

28. School Calendar

Skills: **Desktop Publishing**—entering text or importing a text document into a text frame, changing text (style, size, font type, alignment, and spacing), moving a text frame, importing and customizing graphics (resize, flip, move, copy), selecting a page layout, and saving and printing a document.

Objectives: To become familiar with and use desktop publishing or stationery software. To use small- and large-group cooperative learning techniques to create a class calendar.

Level: Beginner.

Time Required: Three class periods.

Group Size: Three to six students. The class will also be working as one large group.

Materials Needed: At least one computer per group with desktop publishing and word processing capabilities, clip art, and a printer.

Procedure: Students create a class calendar. After you divide the students into six small groups, they brainstorm for ideas to include in their calendar. As a large group, the class votes on the suggestions. You then assign each small group two months of the year. It is their responsibility to fulfill the calendar requirements for those two months. The class then combines their work. You will need a printed copy of the calendar for each student.

Evaluation: Evaluate students based on small group performance, interaction with the other groups, and the final quality of the calendar.

Special Tips: If you are using this activity in the middle of the year, have the students create a calendar for the remaining months or for next year.

While this activity can be done with a desktop publishing program, it is much easier with a stationery program (such as PrintShop or Print Master) or a more professional calendar-generating program (such as Calendar Creator Plus). A stationery program is best for younger students, while older ones can use a desktop publishing or a more professional calendar-generating program.

Use stationery software to create other printed items such as letterhead, signs, cards, and banners. Have the students create these items for themselves and/or for other people. Students could sell some of the items at a profit to earn money for the computer room and/or school.

Have each group create a cover page for the calendar. Other classes or teachers can vote on which cover page gets attached to the front of the calendar.

School Calendar

Most of the calendars you see hanging around a school have pictures of cats and dogs, scenes from national parks, whales and dolphins, or silly cartoons. These calendars are cute, but are they very helpful?

Today your class is going to start designing your own calendar—a calendar designed for students, by students. After your teacher has divided you into six small groups, start discussing in your group what should be on and in your calendar. Create a list of ideas. Should everyone's birthday be on the calendar? what about holidays? what about the vacation schedule? what about the picture or graphic for each month?

Record your list on the computer, using word processing software. When you are finished, hand the list in to your teacher. Your teacher will take all the different groups' lists, eliminate the repeated items, and then present all the ideas to the class. The class will vote on each item. When the voting is complete and the list narrowed down, your teacher will assign each group two of the twelve months. You and your group are responsible for completing all the requirements for your assigned months.

Get started by dividing the workload. Some of you open or create the monthly calendar format in the desktop publishing or stationery software. Some of you conduct research on birthdays, school events, and such, and some of you work on the needed graphics.

Each monthly layout must contain the following:

- a graphic in at least three days of the month
- text information in at least five days of the month
- a top frame that contains at least one graphic and text
- a bottom frame that contains at least one graphic and text

Once your group has completed your two required months, see if one of the other groups needs some help. Remember, this is a large-group project as well as a small-group project. When all of the groups have finished, hand the "whole year" in to your teacher.

Your teacher will tally grades and print the calendar. If you wish to share your calendar outside of your classroom, you will need to sell the calendars to cover printing expenses. This would also be a great way to earn money for the computer room and/or the school.

29. Political Reporters

Skills: (1) **Word Processing**—starting a new document, editing, spell checking, saving and opening a file, and printing. (2) **Desktop Publishing**—importing a text document into a text frame, changing text (style, size, font type, alignment, and spacing), moving a text frame, importing and customizing graphics (resize, flip, move, copy), selecting a page layout, and saving and printing a document.

Objectives: To use desktop publishing software to lay out a newspaper article. To use small-group interaction to create a newspaper article.

Level: Intermediate.

Time Required: Three class periods.

Group Size: Three to six students.

Materials Needed: One computer per group with word processing and desktop publishing capabilities. Clip art and a printer. Access to a bulletin board service or the Internet if possible, other research resources if not.

Procedure: Desktop publishing software is the ideal tool for newspaper article writing. In this activity, cooperative learning groups write a newspaper article dealing with student-related politics. Each group chooses, researches, and writes one article. Students write using a word processing program. Once the article is completed, students import the word processing file into a desktop publishing document. Students then lay out each article in a two-column format, not longer than one full page; they can add one to three graphics. Students hand in their completed articles for grading.

Evaluation: Evaluate students based on small-group interaction, research techniques, and desktop publishing use.

Special Tips: Have plenty of newspapers on hand, especially the political section. Students can use the articles as models.

This is an excellent activity to teach cooperatively with an English teacher and/or the student newspaper advisor.

Politics does not have to be the subject of choice. For example, how about sports, entertainment, or business?

Create a political newspaper containing the articles from all groups in every class.

Name _____ Date _____

Political Reporters

Many students say, "Politics—yuck!" Why should any young person be interested in politics and government? For one thing, if you are currently attending a public school, you are attending a government institution. Even if you are attending a private school, your school may be funded in part by the government. By walking through those doors every day, you are affected by politics.

In this activity, you will play the role of a political reporter. Each small group is responsible for reporting on a subject related to students and politics. The group will write an article as if it were really going to appear in a local or national newspaper. In a two-column format, each article should fit between one half and three quarters of a full page, before any graphics are added. All the issues must be current and related to school-aged young people. Here's a list of possible subject areas:

- recent decisions of the local school board

- politics and the environment

- guns in school and new laws

- cutbacks in extracurricular activities

- cutbacks in the school lunch program

- peer pressure

- young people in the news (superathletes, super brains, special talent, etc.)

Once your group has chosen a subject, start researching. If possible, access a bulletin board service or the Internet to receive the latest information on your subject. You can also use computerized or printed magazine and newspaper indexes. Remember, all good newspaper articles answer the following questions: who, what, where, when, why, and how?

After your group has collected enough information for a substantial newspaper article, start writing the article as a group into a word processing document. Spell check the document and proofread a printout. Make any changes and save the final updates.

Exit the word processor and load the desktop publishing program. Set the page layout to a two-column format and import the article into the left column. Full justify all paragraphs, and keep the text in a size 12 font. The title should be centered, boldfaced, and in a size 14 to 16 font of your choice. The article should contain at least one graphic but no more than three. Make sure all text wraps around any graphic.

Upon completion, show your teacher a screen preview before printing. Print out the article, and proofread it carefully. Update any mistakes, get a final printout, and hand it in to your teacher.

30. Student Newspaper

Skills: (1) **Word Processing**—starting a new document, editing, spell checking, saving and opening a file, and printing. (2) **Desktop Publishing**—importing a text document into a text frame, changing text (style, size, font type, alignment, and spacing), moving a text frame, importing and customizing graphics (resize, flip, move, copy), selecting a page layout, and saving and printing a document.

Objectives: To create a class newspaper using desktop publishing software and small-group cooperative learning techniques.

Level: Advanced.

Group Size: Three to six students.

Time Required: Estimate of five class periods assuming that the students are very familiar with the desktop publishing software.

Materials Needed: At least one computer per group with word processing and desktop publishing capabilities. Because students will be doing some individual work, one computer per student would be ideal. In addition, access to a bulletin board service and/or the Internet would greatly assist the students in research. Students who wish to create their own graphics may need drawing/painting software. Clip art and a printer are also needed.

Procedure: As a spin-off of the "Political Reporters" activity, this lesson is designed to create a complete newspaper. Each group chooses a section of a newspaper to research and write articles for. Each student writes at least one article using a word processor and desktop publishing software. Groups hand their completed newspaper sections in to you for evaluation and printing. Give every student a copy of the class newspaper.

Evaluation: Evaluate students based on small-group interaction, researching skills, desktop publishing use, and the final product.

Special Tips: Have plenty of newspapers on hand for students to use as models.

Allow time for groups to complete necessary research or interviews that might need to take place outside of the classroom.

This is an excellent activity to teach cooperatively with an English teacher and/or the student newspaper advisor.

Have each group create a banner for their section of the paper. If there is time, have each group decide on a name for the paper and create a banner for the front page. Have the class decide which banner will make the cover.

Name _____ Date _____

Student Newspaper

Writing a student newspaper would be an enormous amount of work for one person. In this activity you work in groups to create one student newspaper. This way, the task is not so difficult—it may even be interesting and fun!

The chief editor, publisher, and owner of your newspaper is your teacher, who gives all final approvals. So, after your editor has assigned you to a group, decide on and seek approval of one of the following areas your group can manage:

- international news
- state news
- local or city news

- sports
- entertainment
- school news

If your group creates its own area of interest, it must have your editor's approval.

Once your group has gotten your editor's OK, start conducting research. Each member of the team must write *at least one* article in the chosen area. Work together in assigning article subjects; make sure none of you are writing about the same thing. Do not forget about possible graphics. Using bulletin board services and the Internet is a quick way to collect information. Computerized and printed magazine and newspaper indexes are other research resources.

After your group has collected enough information, start writing the articles in separate word processing documents. Be sure to spell check each document and proofread the printouts. Make any changes and save the final updates.

Exit the word processor and load the desktop publishing program. Set the page layout to a two- or three-column format, and import each article into the text frame, starting in the left column. Full-justify all paragraphs, and keep the text in a size 12 font. The title should be centered, boldfaced, and in a size 14 to 16 font of your choice. Most articles should contain at least one graphic but no more than three. Make sure the text wraps around any graphic. To get an authentic look to your layout, model closely to real newspapers.

Once your group has completed your section of the newspaper, hand it in for editing. Your editor/teacher may ask you to make some changes. Do not be discouraged—this happens in real life, too. Once improvements are made, hand the section in once more. Your teacher will collect all the sections and make copies for the whole class.

As a class, discuss the final product. What do you like best about your newspaper? What do you like the least? What could have been done to improve it? What important items were left out? What desktop publishing techniques were used well, and how did that group do it? What other types of technology did some of the groups use?

CHAPTER 6

CD-ROM and Educational Software

31. CD-ROM Scavenger Hunt

Skills: (1) **CD-ROM**—word searches, playing sound and animation clips, and displaying pictures, maps, and corresponding text frames. (2) **Word Processing**—starting a new document, editing, spell checking, performing block operations, saving and opening a file, and printing.

Objectives: To expose students to CD-ROM programs through the use of game playing. To use small-group cooperation to problem solve.

Level: Beginning.

Time Required: Three class periods.

Group Size: Three or more students per group, but no more than four groups per class. If you have a limited number of CD-ROM stations, divide the class by the number of stations you have. If you have only one CD-ROM station, you can rotate CD-ROM activities with other assignments.

Materials Needed: One computer with CD-ROM capabilities per group and an optional computer to use for creating the questions and answers in a word processing document. CD-ROM programs of your choice, preferably limited to four.

Procedure: Small groups send other small groups on a scavenger hunt, conducted in CD-ROM reference programs such as encyclopedias, atlases, and almanacs. Each group develops 10 questions that can only be answered by using CD-ROM programs. The groups exchange questions. The first group to answer all the questions correctly wins.

Evaluation: Evaluate students on the questions they present to another group, the success of answering the questions given to them, and how the group cooperates as a team.

Special Tips: This is a high-participation activity for the teacher. You will be acting as consultant as well as judge. However, it is fun! You'll be surprised at what great questions the kids can come up with.

Some of the questions the students write will be too vague. Each question needs at least *one* word that students can use to do a search. Push students to be as creative as they can be, using as many tools available with each program as possible. Questions could include displaying pictures, maps, time lines, and animation as well as playing sounds, music, and speeches.

Each group must have at least two questions from each program.

Allow a fixed amount of time per program. When the time is up, have each group set the software back to the main menu screen and then rotate to another CD-ROM station. This saves a lot of time and is easier than having each group log into a new program.

Create the questions for the hunt yourself. This will not only save time but also give you more control over what the students are researching.

CD-ROM Scavenger Hunt

Everyone is going hunting! Don't worry about carrying a gun or wearing camouflage clothing. You're going hunting with a keyboard and a mouse. And where are you going hunting? Right in your own technology room, on a computer and in CD-ROM programs.

After your teacher has divided you into groups, familiarize yourself with the CD-ROM programs your teacher has assigned. Get to know the programs; they're the hunting grounds!

The object of this activity is to send and be sent on a scavenger hunt. As a group, you will come up with 10 questions that can only be answered by using the CD-ROM programs. You will then give these questions to another group in your class. In return, your team will receive questions from a different group. The first team to answer all of the questions wins!

To start the game, your group needs to write 10 questions. Search your CD-ROM programs for interesting or even bizarre items. Here are some sample questions:

- How small is the smallest hummingbird?
- How large is a soccer field?
- Where is the country of Angola?
- Who is Atlas, and what did he carry on his back?
- What day of the year is Boxing Day?
- Who is the founder of the Microsoft Corporation?

If you are using more than one CD-ROM program, be sure to rearrange the questions so that all those from one program are not listed together. It's challenging for a group not only to locate an answer in a program but also to figure out which program is needed.

Along with each question, you must prepare some hints which your teacher may require you to give. You must also write an answer key on a separate page, including each answer, the name of the CD-ROM program used, and the steps your group took to locate the answer.

Once you have finished your questions, hand them in to your teacher for approval. Your teacher may ask you to be a little more specific on some of the questions. When all the groups have finished, your teacher will conduct the question exchange.

Now the game really begins! As quickly and as efficiently as possible, answer all the questions. Your teacher will tell you how many computer terminals you may use. Remember, you are a *team*. Work together. Answer as many questions as you can. If you get stuck, consult your teacher and ask to be granted a hint. Your teacher will make the final decision.

When you have finished answering all the questions, present the answers to the appropriate group. They will make sure your answers are correct. Your teacher will settle any dispute. The first team to answer all the questions correctly wins! Each group must finish the scavenger hunt to receive a grade.

The following project is made up of six activities. Each activity calls for CD-ROM programs. Most of the lessons allow for flexibility in choice of CD-ROM reference programs. As in the library, it doesn't really matter which brand of encyclopedias are on hand, just that there *is* a set of encyclopedias. CD-ROM reference programs that will come in handy are:

encyclopedias	time line programs
geography programs	almanacs
atlases	history programs

32. Follow an Explorer: Part I—The Choice

Skills: **CD-ROM**—word searches, playing sound and animation clips, and displaying pictures, maps, and corresponding text frames.

Objectives: To search the contents of a CD-ROM software program. To learn about explorers through the cooperative learning process.

Level: Intermediate.

Time Required: One class period.

Group Size: Three to six students.

Materials Needed: One computer with CD-ROM capabilities per group. Optional: more than one computer per group. If this is not possible, use the standard research tools.

Procedure: Students choose an explorer. Minimal research is required but encouraged. The group must know if there is enough information about the explorer and the expedition to finish the rest of the activities. Students fill out the choice worksheet and hand it in to you for approval.

Evaluation: Evaluate students based on their timely decision-making skills.

Special Tips: You are likely to run into the problem of more than one group wanting to follow the same explorer. Allow this only if the explorer went on more than one expedition. Otherwise, first come, first served.

Make sure the students choose well-documented explorers. One paragraph in a CD-ROM encyclopedia is not enough information to complete the following activities.

Follow an Explorer: Part I—The Choice

Imagine what it was like for Lewis and Clark to explore our nation when it was young. Place yourself on Sir John Franklin's ship in the Arctic searching for the Northwest Passage. Or picture yourself standing on the summit of Mount Everest with Sir Edmund Hillary. What about Columbus, Marco Polo, and Magellan? The list goes on and on; so many adventures with so many great adventurers.

Your role as a group in this activity is to follow the route of a great explorer. Choose an explorer whom everyone in the group is interested in researching. The group may need to spend some time on the computer, using CD-ROM encyclopedias and looking at a number of different explorers. Once your team has come to a consensus, complete the following questionnaire for your teacher.

Note: If your chosen explorer has been on more than one expedition, choose only one of those adventures.

Group Members' Names: _____

_____

_____

_____

_____

_____

_____

_____

_____

_____

_____

_____

Name of Chosen Explorer: _____

Dates of Exploration: _____

Teacher's Initials for Approval: _____

33. Follow an Explorer: Part II—The Map

Skills: (1) **CD-ROM**—word and map searches, displaying maps and corresponding text frames, saving a map as a graphic file, and printing a map. (2) **Drawing/Painting** (optional)—importing a map file, using standard tools either to draw a map or make additions to a map file.

Objectives: To create a map using information from CD-ROM encyclopedias. To work together in a group setting to develop a map of an explorer's travels.

Level: Intermediate.

Time Required: Two class periods.

Group Size: Three to six students.

Materials Needed: One computer with CD-ROM capabilities per group. Optional: more than one computer per group. If you do not have CD-ROM encyclopedias, direct the students to use regular encyclopedias. Geography software, such as PC USA and PC World, would be a great help to the students; however, if you do not have geography software, simply have the students create the maps by using draw/paint software or by hand.

Procedure: Students create a map of the explorer's expedition. Using CD-ROM programs, each group conducts research and gathers information about the path the explorer took. To draw the map, students could use other software programs or conventional means.

Evaluation: Evaluate students based on group interaction and the final product.

Special Tips: If you do not have the helpful software, make sure you provide more conventional material for your students (paper, tag board, scissors, miscellaneous drawing utensils, etc.).

If you have geography software, students may need a lesson on or a review of the map-drawing techniques.

If the program allows printing of maps, make sure to preview all maps before students send them to the printer. You can use a sign-up sheet for print-outs and have students complete their printouts during class, or you can print the maps at a later date. Train a student helper to assist you with the printouts.

Check whether the program will save a map as a graphic file. If so, students can save a map to their disk and import it into a drawing/painting or desktop publishing program where they can make additions to the map. Once the graphic is complete, it can even be imported into a presentation software program to be displayed to the class on a large-screen monitor.

Display the maps for current and future classes to see.

Students could create their map in a multimedia environment.

Name _____ Date _____

Follow an Explorer: Part II—The Map

Where did your explorer explore? Answer this question by creating a map that highlights your explorer's expedition. Maps of the past have evolved over the years; rivers have changed course, countries have been formed or overthrown, and boundaries have been redrawn. Your group has the option to create a map of the past or create a modern-looking map. Just make sure the course the explorer took is clearly defined on your map.

Once you have an idea what your group's map should look like, start creating it. Use your CD-ROM encyclopedia to gather the information you need for the map. Use your geography software or drawing/painting software to help you create the map. Whichever you choose, the following items must appear on the map:

1. the continent, country, or body of water that was explored

2. major geographical items (mountains, rivers, lakes, etc.)

3. the course taken by the explorer

4. mileage gauge (estimation)

5. name of expedition and explorer

6. dates of expedition

Present your map to your teacher for grading.

34. Follow an Explorer: Part III— The Time Line

Skills: (1) **CD-ROM**—word and time line searches, displaying time lines and corresponding text frames, saving a map as a graphic file, and printing a map. (2) Creating a time line using a **drawing/painting** program, a **word processing** program, or (optional) a **multimedia presentation** program.

Objectives: To use CD-ROM technology and small-group participation to create a time line.

Level: Intermediate.

Time Required: Two class periods.

Group Size: Three to six students.

Materials Needed: One computer with CD-ROM capabilities per group. Optional: more than one computer per group. If you do not have CD-ROM encyclopedias, direct the students to use printed ones. Time line software, such as Tom Snyder's Timeline, would be a great help to the students; otherwise, simply have the students create the time lines by hand or by using drawing/painting or word processing software. Students may need to write explanations of important dates on a word processor.

Procedure: Expeditions often took years to complete. Students will better understand this if they see a visual representation. So, each group creates a time line representation of the expedition they are studying, using CD-ROM reference programs to obtain all essential information. To draw the time line, students can use time line software, such as Tom Snyder's Timeline, or conventional means.

Evaluation: Evaluate students based on group interaction and research collection skills as well as on the end product, including the time line and date explanations.

Special Tips: The date explanations are required so the students don't just slap a bunch of dates up on a time line. There has to be a significant reason for each date.

If the students are writing their explanations in a word processing document or a time line program, encourage them to have the documents up and running at the same time.

Have the different groups work together and arrange all the time lines by date on a bulletin board. Which explorers were on their expeditions at the same time? Which explorations were first? Which explorations were last?

Have advanced classes create the time line in a multimedia presentation program such as Hyper-Card or Linkway. Presentations of each time line will be made on a large-screen monitor. Students can create hypertext links from the time line to text and graphic frames.

Name _____   Date _____

Follow an Explorer: Part III—The Time Line

How long did it take your explorer to finish the expedition? Did it take him or her days, months, years? How long was he or she away from family and friends?

Your group could simply answer these questions by spewing off some boring dates. How interesting is that? Instead, in this activity, your group is going to make a time line to illustrate the length of time it took your explorer to finish the expedition.

Using CD-ROM encyclopedias, research and collect the important dates of the expedition. Each time line must include *at least 10* important dates. Explanations of the importance of these dates may appear directly on the time line or in a separate word processing document. The following days are only suggestions but may help you get started:

- the day the expedition started

- the day the expedition almost failed

- the day or days of major discoveries

- the day your explorer or one of the team members took ill or died

- the day your explorer met special people or animals

- the day the expedition was completed

Once your group has collected all the valuable facts, start making the time line. Use available time line software to help you draw and enter information. Work together, making sure you use all the information and enter it correctly. Adding color and pictures is optional but encouraged.

When you are finished, present your time line to your teacher for grading.

35. Follow an Explorer: Part IV— The Journal

Skills: (1) **CD-ROM**—word searches, playing sound and animation clips, and displaying pictures, maps, and corresponding text frames.
(2) **Word Processing**—starting a new document, editing, spell checking, performing block operations, saving and opening a file, and printing.
(3) **Drawing/Painting** or **Stationery** program—creating a cover page.

Objectives: To have the students use CD-ROM technology and a cooperative learning setting in order to create a journal.

Level: Intermediate.

Time Required: Three class periods.

Group Size: Three to six students.

Materials Needed: One computer with CD-ROM capabilities per group. If you do not have CD-ROM encyclopedias, direct the students to use printed encyclopedias. For the actual writing of journal entries, each student should at some time have access to her or his own computer terminal with word processing capabilities. Drawing/ painting or stationery software (such as PrintShop) would be helpful for creating the cover page of the journal.

Procedure: Using CD-ROM reference programs, students conduct research in order to write journal entries as if they were the explorers themselves. Each student writes at least two journal entries, which are discussed and approved by the rest of the group. The group then combines the entries into one journal.

Evaluation: Evaluate students based on group interaction, individual journal entries, and the final project as a whole.

Special Tips: Suggest to the students that they use the same dates that appear on the time line.

To save time, make the cover page optional.

For more control over the activity, assign the students specific days to write about—for example, the first day of the expedition, and the last day of the expedition, the day of discovery.

Name _____ Date _____

Follow an Explorer: Part IV—The Journal

At the time, most of the great explorers knew they were making history. For posterity's sake, many of them kept a journal. Some of them did this for selfish reasons; they wanted to be famous and remembered forever. Others kept a journal for unselfish reasons; they wanted history to be recorded correctly. Whatever their reasons, their journals are undeniably interesting.

In this activity, your group will write journal entries as if you were the actual explorer. Use information from CD-ROM encyclopedias to help you get the facts straight, and use your imaginations to fill in the blanks. It is OK to stretch the truth a bit. After all, you can't actually get inside the explorer's mind.

Each team member is required to write two journal entries. Discuss your ideas with the rest of the group, and try to eliminate overlapping topics. The following are only suggestions:

- What major event happened today?

- Whom did you meet today?

- What animals did you see today?

- How do you feel today—physically and emotionally?

- When you look around, what do you see?

- What has been one of the major hardships of the expedition?

- What has been one of the triumphs of the expedition?

After discussing your ideas with the group and researching on CD-ROM, start writing the entries. Use your word processor. You may wish to choose a script font, so what you type looks like handwriting. When the whole group has finished, place the entries in chronological order. Create a cover for the journal by using drawing/painting software or a stationery program such as PrintShop.

When the journal is finished, turn it in to your teacher for grading.

36. Follow an Explorer: Part V— The Past and Future Essays

Skills: (1) **CD-ROM**—word searches, playing sound and animation clips, and displaying pictures, maps, and corresponding text frames. (2) **Word Processing**—starting a new document, editing, spell checking, performing block operations, saving and opening a file, and printing.

Objectives: To use CD-ROM encyclopedias. To collect information for writing essays about an explorer. To utilize cooperative learning techniques to write essays.

Level: Advanced.

Time Required: Two class periods.

Group Size: Three to six students.

Materials Needed: One computer with CD-ROM capabilities per group. Optional: more than one computer per group. If you do not have CD-ROM encyclopedias, direct the students to use regular encyclopedias. At least two computer terminals with word processing capabilities for each group, as well as a printer.

Procedure: Each group writes two essays: One is about the explorer's past; the second is about the explorer's impact on the future. Students use CD-ROM reference programs to conduct research needed to write the essays.

Evaluation: Evaluate students based on research techniques, group interaction, and the final essays.

Special Tips: Students are more likely to write the essays together if they do the research together. Gathering information is essential in this exercise. If everyone participates in the gathering process, they will more than likely participate in the sharing process.

Note that essay #2 may look easy but often gives students trouble. In this essay, students need to combine fact with opinion. Emphasize to the students that in many ways there is no wrong answer for this essay.

Show students how to copy text information from a CD-ROM encyclopedia to a word processing document. One method is to select the text (highlight it), copy it to the clipboard, and paste it from the clipboard into the word processing document. Another method is to select the text and save it to a disk, then import the text file (under ASCII format) into a word processing document.

If you are pressed for time, have students write only one essay. Or do not require the actual writing; instead, have students take notes and present the information as part of their final project.

Follow an Explorer: Part V—The Past and Future Essays

In this activity, your group writes two essays about an explorer. Everyone may decide to work on both essays, or you may decide to divide the work among yourselves. Use your CD-ROM encyclopedias to help you with the research. Use your word processing software to take notes and compose the essays.

Essay #1: The Past

Why did this person become an explorer?

Have you asked that question yet? Have you figured it out on your own? What do the expert historians have to say about it? Did the explorer's parents influence him or her? Did a teacher influence the young explorer? As a child or teen, was the explorer ever found wandering around the neighborhood or investigating the countryside? Was this person a born explorer?

Use your CD-ROM encyclopedias to gather information about your explorer's background. Here are some items you may wish to include in your essay:

- major childhood events
- financial circumstances
- education
- support from family, friends, government, etc.
- influences (parents, relatives, teachers, friends, religion, government, etc.)

Essay #2: Future Essay

How did your explorer influence the future?

Many explorers had a profound effect on the future of the world. Consider, for example, Columbus "discovering" America. How many of us would be where we are today without Columbus and his historic exploration? How would the Americas have developed if Columbus had not made his voyage and discovery? Similarly, what kind of impact did your explorer have on the world?

Use your CD-ROM encyclopedias to help you with this essay. However, you are going to have to do some thinking for yourselves. Talk among yourselves. What are your opinions?

Before handing your essays in for grading, have everyone in the group read them over for editing purposes. Using a word processor makes this type of editing process easier. Make sure to use the spell checker as well as the thesaurus. When you have finished editing, turn your essays in to be graded.

37. Follow an Explorer: Part VI—The Presentation

Skills: (1) **CD-ROM**—word searches, playing sound and animation clips, and displaying pictures, maps, and corresponding text frames.
(2) **Word Processing**—starting a new document, editing, spell checking, performing block operations, saving and opening a file, and printing.
(3) **Drawing/Painting** or **Stationery** program—creating a cover page for each section of the presentation along with any other additional information.
(4) **Multimedia Presentation Software**—creating hypertext links to different areas of the presentation and importing text and graphical information.

Objectives: To use CD-ROM encyclopedias to gather information. To use small-group interaction to put together and present information.

Level: Advanced.

Time Required: Three class periods.

Group Size: Three to six students.

Materials Needed: One computer with CD-ROM capabilities per group. Optional: more than one computer per group for research. If you do not have CD-ROM encyclopedias, direct the students to use printed encyclopedias. Multimedia software and a large-screen monitor would be helpful. To create hard-copy visual aids, students may wish to use drawing/painting software, desktop publishing software, geography software, and so on. Word processing software would be helpful for note taking.

Procedure: In this final explorer activity, students present all their research to the rest of the class. By using a wide variety of CD-ROM and educational software, students can make creative additions to their research. They are encouraged to add visual aids and written items. A list of suggestions is provided for the students.

Evaluation: Evaluate students based on research skills, group interaction, group presentation skills, and the final group product.

Special Tips: Encourage the students to go all out, using all the computer technology available to them to make their presentations interesting and visually pleasing.

Note that if students use multimedia presentation software, it may take them longer to put their presentations together. However, the results will be well worth the time spent.

Encourage other teachers and administrators to attend the presentations. Teachers might see a use for technology in their classrooms, and administrators love seeing technology used to its fullest. These types of presentations help to sell your program and could lead to more hardware and software purchases.

Be flexible with the requirements. You may want to require only three items, or you may want to require all of the items, including the suggestions.

Name _____ Date _____

Follow an Explorer: Part VI—The Presentation

Once your group has finished Parts I through V of the "Follow an Explorer" activities, the final step is to present all your research to the rest of the class. You may choose to do a multimedia presentation using a large-screen monitor, or you may choose to do a more conventional presentation using visual aids. However, to create your visual aids, try using as much computer technology as possible, such as drawing/painting software, desktop publishing software, and geography software.

Divide the presentation as equally as possible; every group member must take a turn presenting some of the group's research. Items that *must* appear or be discussed in the presentation are:

1. the map

2. the time line

3. some fictional student journal entries

4. key thoughts from the essays

Any additions to the presentation are encouraged and welcomed. Use your CD-ROM encyclopedias to help you with additional information. Here are some suggestions:

- pictures of the explorer

- pictures of the traveled landscape or seascape

- pictures of people and/or animals the explorer met

- actual journal entries written by the explorer

- letters written by the explorer

- letters written to the explorer

- accounts of what happened to the explorer *after* the exploration

Your group will be graded on the information in the presentation, group participation, and group cooperation. Good luck!

38. Where Is She?

Skills: **CD-ROM or software**—word searches, playing sound and animation clips, and displaying pictures, maps, and corresponding text frames.

Objectives: To use and become familiar with CD-ROM programs. To conduct research and problem solve in a small-group setting.

Level: Beginning.

Group Size: At least three students.

Time Required: As a required lesson, this varies according to teacher requirements. It is possible to use this activity during free time as well. It is a great fill-in activity because students can easily start, stop, and restart it.

Materials Needed: One computer with Where in the World Is Carmen Sandiego? and/or Where in the USA Is Carmen Sandiego? software for each group, plus separate computers with reference programs running.

Procedure: Students love to play the computer game Where in the World Is Carmen Sandiego? In this activity, students are required to play the game in a group setting. In addition, they are only allowed to use reference materials that are software-based. They are not allowed to use conventional research tools. Most groups will solve three to five cases in one class period.

Evaluation: Evaluate students based on research skills, group participation, and success at playing the game. You may not want to grade this activity.

Special Tips: This activity emphasizes research skills. Remind students that they can only use CD-ROM or software programs to conduct research. Many of them will be tempted to use more conventional means of research. Remind them that in the long run, using CD-ROM and software programs is quicker and much more enjoyable.

Because every game will be different, emphasize to the groups that they will not be competing against each other.

Use as many computers as possible for reference tools. Each group should send a member to a specific reference computer to locate the information their group needs.

Using a word processing document adjacent to the Carmen program, have each group log the places they traveled to solve the case along with the software used to research answers.

Where Is She?

Most of you have played the game Where in the World Is Carmen Sandiego? and/or Where in the USA Is Carmen Sandiego? Today, you are going to play it again, except this time there are two major requirements:

1. You must play the game as a team.

2. You can use only CD-ROM and reference software programs as sources of information.

As usual, play as much of the game as possible without using reference materials. As a group, you should do quite well. However, when you get stuck, the only reference materials you can use have to be on CD-ROM or software programs. Some helpful programs fall into the category of encyclopedias, atlases, and almanacs. Use anything as long as it is on a computer. Those are the rules.

Your group should be able to solve three to five cases per class period.

Good luck in finding where Carmen Sandiego is!

39. The 20-Question Illness

Skills: **CD-ROM** or **software**—word searches, playing sound and animation clips, and displaying pictures, graphics, and corresponding text frames.

Objectives: To use and become familiar with CD-ROM programs in the area of science and health. To work within a small-group setting.

Level: Advanced.

Group Size: Three to six students.

Time Required: Depending on your system, time requirements will vary. Things will move faster if all your students have access to a CD-ROM. If you have a network, the question-and-answer time will also move more quickly. You can always limit the time students have to conduct research. This may be especially important during the question-and-answer session.

Materials Needed: CD-ROM or software reference programs dealing with science, health, or medicine. For CD-ROM programs, you will need one computer with CD-ROM capabilities per group. The group *could* use more than one computer for research.

Procedure: Students use CD-ROM software in the area of health and science. Each group chooses a disease or injury, researches it, studies it,

and prepares three written symptoms. These symptoms are shared with the competing team, which then has time to conduct research of their own and ask 20 questions to try to guess the ailment.

Evaluation: Evaluate students based on group research skills and group interaction.

Special Tips: Try cooperatively teaching this activity with the science or health instructor.

As with any topic related to health, students may stray into an inappropriate frame of mind.

You may want to approve of the groups' choices before play begins.

Note that this is an advanced activity, because of the complex vocabulary often used in health-related fields as well as the complex nature of the programs themselves.

This is an ideal activity to play on a network. Students can ask the 20 questions over the network.

The activity may be used in almost any area of study. How about in art: The 20-Question Artist? Or how about in history: The 20-Question President?

Remind the students to keep to appropriate topics.

The 20-Question Illness

In this activity your group is going to diagnose another group's illness. That's right! Every group in your class is either sick or injured, and it is your job to discover what is ailing them.

To begin, you must become sick yourselves. What kind of disease or injury do all of you want to have? Search through your CD-ROM or software reference programs about science, health, or medicine. There must be something you are interested in researching. How about one of the following suggestions:

- ulcers
- common cold
- gout

- influenza
- strep
- mononucleosis

Whatever your group decides, the choice must be unanimous. After the vote is taken, study your disease or affliction carefully. You must be prepared to answer the questions the other group asks you. In addition, you must prepare *three* symptoms to give to the other group as their starting point.

Once you have revealed the three symptoms, the guessing game begins. If you have ever played 20 Questions, you know how the game proceeds. The other group may ask you any yes or no question. You must answer honestly. If you do not know, return to your CD-ROM research, and try to answer the question. If it is impossible to answer, simply reply, "We don't know." Your opponent gets to ask another question in its place. If they ask 20 questions and have not discovered your illness, you win!

Now the examining table is turned. It is your turn to guess. After you have been told the three symptoms, do some research on the CD-ROM reference programs. After you ask one or some questions, do some more research. Feel free to do as much research as time allows. Take turns asking questions. A few of the best starting questions to ask are:

- Is it a disease?
- Is it an injury?

- Is it a virus?
- Is it hereditary?

Take great care in the questions you ask. Work from the general to the specific. As a group, you may want to write a few questions down before you even start asking them. And of course, if you guess the problem before your 20 questions are up, you win!

If you have time to spare or some free time, try your illness out on another group.

40. The Trail Across America

Skills: **CD-ROM**—word searches, playing sound and animation clips, and displaying pictures, maps, and corresponding text frames. (2) **Word Processing**—starting a new document, editing, spell checking, performing block operations, saving and opening a file, and printing.

Objectives: To familiarize students with role-playing and/or geography software. To learn about the Oregon Trail through the use of group inter-action.

Level: Intermediate.

Group Size: The ideal group size is five.

Time Required: Time allowances will vary with the choice of software and assignments. The Oregon Trail program usually takes two days to complete. Allow one additional day to enter information into a word processing document.

Materials Needed: One computer with appropriate software per group, preferably with The Oregon Trail, otherwise use generic geography software. For specific assignments, it may be easier and less time-consuming if each student has her or his own computer. CD-ROM or printed encyclopedias are a must. Word processing software would be beneficial.

Procedure: Using a computer simulation—the educational software program The Oregon Trail produced by MECC—students become familiar with life as a pioneer traveling along the Oregon Trail in 1848. If your school district does not own a copy of The Oregon Trail, create your own trail adventure. Simply use generic geography software, having the students map out the Oregon Trail themselves. Other assignments could include drawing a map and/or creating a time line, writing in a journal, writing an essay describing the landscape, and/or drawing a landscape, writing an essay describing people and animals and/or drawing people and animals, and verbal debates regarding the situation of the pioneer *vs.* the situation of the Native American.

Evaluation: Evaluate students based on group interaction and final products.

Special Tips: Feel free to include any additional activities or handouts that come with The Oregon Trail software. The network version of The Oregon Trail allows each group to represent one wagon of the class wagon train. Therefore, a decision that one group makes will affect all the other groups. Many schools are now playing The Oregon Trail over the Internet. Students of all ages love to play this program.

The students will have to do a great deal of research about the Oregon Trail. You may want to gather some of the introductory materials for them. Make sure information in some format is constantly available to them.

This activity is ideal for co-teaching with the social studies teacher.

Name _____ Date _____

The Trail Across America

Have you ever wondered what it was like to be a pioneer? Have you ever wondered what it was like to travel across America in a covered wagon? In this activity you will gain a better understanding of the people who journeyed along the Oregon Trail, across wild country in 1848, to settle the West. You may be using a program called The Oregon Trail, a computer simulation of one of the greatest adventures in American history. Your group will make "life-or-death" decisions as you attempt to cross over 2000 miles of plains, rivers, and mountains. Your goal is to reach a fertile valley in Oregon where you can have a better life.

Your teacher will divide you into groups. Each group will "travel" together in one wagon, as relatives or close family friends usually did. Using your imaginations, create roles for yourselves. Are you an old lady traveling with her nephew, or an orphan girl traveling with her aunt and uncle? Are you a teenage boy looking for a wife, or an old man traveling to see the Pacific Ocean before he dies? Whomever you decide to be, remember that each group has to have a leader and enough adults to carry the workload. You must discuss your role-playing choice with the rest of the group.

On a computer with word processing software, write an autobiography about your character. If you are having trouble coming up with ideas, the following questions may help you get started:

1. What is your name?

2. Where were you born?

3. How old are you?

4. What do you look like?

5. Why did you or your forebears come to America?

6. Why are you traveling across the United States?

7. Describe your family (consult your fellow group members).

8. Are you scared to travel in a covered wagon?

9. What do you expect to see along the way?

10. What are you going to do once you get to Oregon?

When you have finished your essay, share it with the rest of the group. Your teacher may ask you to share it with the rest of the class. Turn your essay in for credit.

41. Idea City

Skills: (1) Sim City 2000—Saving and opening city files and creating and maintaining a city. (2) **Word Processing**—starting a new document, editing, spell checking, performing block operations, saving and opening a file, and printing.

Objectives: To use the educational software program Sim City 2000 to simulate the creating and maintaining of a city. To use the small-group decision-making process.

Level: Advanced.

Group Size: Three to four students.

Time Required: Three to five days. This activity can extend over a long period of time.

Materials Needed: One computer per group with word processing capabilities and the software program Sim City 2000.

Procedure: Students use the software program Sim City 2000, a simulation game in which the users plan, design, and run a city. In the process, students use cooperative decision-making skills. After students have created their city, they answer a number of questions designed for group evaluation. Class discussion of the process is encouraged.

Evaluation: Evaluate students based on their acquired familiarity with Sim City 2000, small group participation, and the answers to the given questions.

Special Tips: Read the introduction in the Sim City 2000 manual to the class before starting the activity. Have the manual available for each group to reference.

Have each group save their city on a student disk, not on the hard drive of the computer. This will save room on your computer and will reduce the chances of other students' changing the characteristics of a city.

Make sure each group member has the opportunity to use the program.

Require new users to the program to complete one or all of the tutorials.

This software program was designed for individual use. Students love to play with it on their own. It is a great educational game for students to use during free time.

Require students to take on certain roles. For example, one group member could be the "environmentalist," another group member the "greedy industrialist," and so on.

Have students complete one or more of the predefined scenarios, which include a prebuilt city, a problem to solve or disaster to face, a goal to reach, and a time limit to meet.

Name _____ Date _____

Idea City

Imagine what it would be like to create your own city. You would probably feel something like a king or queen. To have such power, such control, could be a little overwhelming. So imagine creating a city with the help of friends.

In this activity, you and your group are going to create a city using the software program Sim City 2000. The group will make all major decisions. Your success or failure will be a shared responsibility.

After your teacher has installed Sim City 2000 onto your computers, start familiarizing yourselves with the software by examining the three tutorials: The Basics, Landscape Engineering, and Advanced Features. If you wish, one or two group members could be responsible for the information in each tutorial.

As a group, decide on which type of environment you wish to build: rural town, small city, or megalopolis. Sim City 2000 is primarily a building activity; however, it offers some opportunities to destroy. All destruction decisions, unless they happen by chance, must also be made by the group.

Once you have created a city, answer the following questions as a group in a separate word processing document:

1. What type of city did your group create?

2. What special features does your city have?

3. What feature are you most proud of?

4. What disasters happened along the way?

5. How is your financial situation?

6. Is this a city you would like to live in?

7. Which group decision was the best?

8. Which group decision was the most disastrous?

9. In what ways did sharing the responsibility of building a city with a group make it easier?

10. In what ways did sharing the responsibility of building a city with a group make it harder?

After you have answered the above questions, hand them in to your teacher for grading. Discuss your city successes and failures with the rest of the groups.

CHAPTER 7

Programming

42. Sketch and Draw Those Points and Lines

Skills: **Programming**—writing a small graphic program, drawing points and lines, and reading coordinates from graph paper.

Objectives: To familiarize students with programming. To plot points and lines in the graphics environment of a programming language. To write small programs that draw simple designs. To understand the coordinate system of a graphic screen of a programming language. To use small-group cooperation for programming purposes.

Level: Beginning.

Time Required: Two class periods.

Group Size: Three or more students.

Materials Needed: One computer per group. A programming language that can plot points and lines, such as LOGO, BASIC, Pascal, or C. Graph paper containing the coordinates of the graphic page you plan to use.

Procedure: Each group draws five simple designs using a programming language. The designs are made up of only points and lines. This activity gives your students a chance to understand the coordinate system of a graphic screen while working in a programming environment. Using graphics is an excellent way of introducing programming to your students. While programming can seem confusing, students will enjoy it and stay more focused on the topic when working in a graphics setting. Groups will show you the final screen output for each program for your approval and initialing.

Evaluation: Evaluate students on the number of graphic designs completed and how the group cooperates as a team.

Special Tips: Review the use of background and line color statements. In some languages, this can become confusing. Include the color statements and color numbers at the top of each sheet of graph paper.

Create a few sample programs for each group to enter before starting this activity. This will give your students a chance to become familiar with the programming environment, especially debugging mistakes they make on entering the lines of code.

To save time, have students complete only the first four designs and do the last design for extra credit.

Allow groups to come up with their own flag design.

Sketch and Draw Those Points and Lines

In this activity you have the opportunity to use a programming language to draw points and lines on the screen. Your group will actually write five programs. Below are a set of designs that you will complete. Before writing each program, sketch each design on a piece of graph paper and review the coordinate system with each member in your group. Once everyone understands the coordinate system, your group is ready to go off and write the program that will produce the sketched output. Feel free to experiment with background and line colors. Make sure each member of your group gets a chance to enter some code. The goal is that by the end of the activity, everyone in your group can write a program that draws points and lines on the graphic screen.

As you complete each design, show it to your teacher, who will approve and initial it.

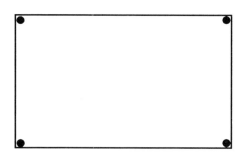 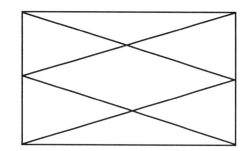

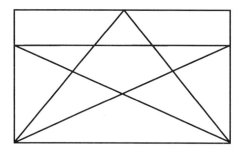 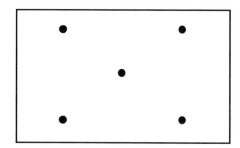

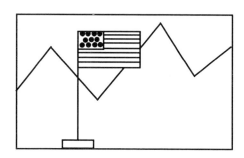

       61 Cooperative Learning Activities for Computer Classrooms

43. Drawing Rectangles and Circles

Skills: **Programming**—writing a small graphic program, drawing rectangles and circles, and reading coordinates from graph paper.

Objectives: To familiarize students with programming. To draw rectangles and circles in the graphics environment of a programming language. To write small programs that draw simple designs. To understand the coordinate system of a graphic screen of a programming language. To use small-group cooperative learning techniques.

Level: Beginning.

Time Required: Two class periods.

Group Size: Three or more students.

Materials Needed: One computer per group. A programming language that can draw rectangles and circles such as LOGO, BASIC, Pascal, or C. (**Note:** Applesoft BASIC used with the Apple II computer does not contain either a rectangle or a circle statement.) Graph paper containing the coordinates of the graphic page you plan to use.

Procedure: Students use their programming skills to draw designs made up of only rectangles and circles. Students first sketch each design onto graph paper. Once the sketches are completed, students transform the coordinates needed to draw the rectangles and circles into computer code. Groups will show you the final screen output for each program for your approval and initialing.

Evaluation: Evaluate students on the number of graphic designs completed and how the group cooperates as a team.

Special Tips: Include information about filling or painting along with a few examples.

Leave programming manuals out where a group can have access to them for reference purposes. You could even give each group a manual to use during the activity.

To save time, have students complete each design without painting or filling in the areas. Have students save each program as a separate file. Then, those groups that finish early can load in the files and experiment with the fill or paint statements.

Name _____   Date _____

Drawing Rectangles and Circles

The five designs below can all be drawn with rectangles and circles. As a group, your job is to sketch each design on graph paper and then plot it on the screen. Write each design as a separate program. Feel free to experiment with background and line colors. If the language that you are using allows it, try filling or painting the areas in different colors and/or patterns. Make sure each member of your group gets a chance at entering some code. The goal is that by the end of the activity, everyone in your group can write a program that draws rectangles and circles on the graphic screen.

As you complete each design, show it to your teacher, who will approve and initial it.

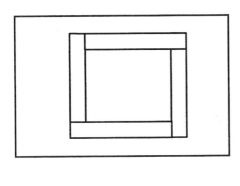
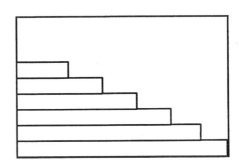

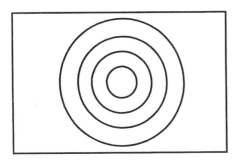
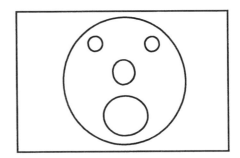

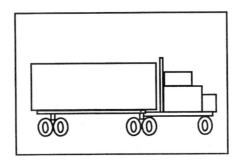

44. The Top-of-the-Line Computer

Skills: **Programming**—writing a graphic program, drawing (points, lines, rectangles, and circles), and reading coordinates from graph paper.

Objectives: To familiarize students with programming. To plot points and lines in the graphics environment of a programming language. To write a larger program that utilizes the graphic statements that draw points, lines, rectangles, and circles. To understand the coordinate system of a graphic screen of a programming language. To use small-group cooperation to perform programming skills.

Level: Beginning.

Time Required: Three class periods.

Group Size: Three or more students.

Materials Needed: One computer per group. A programming language that can draw points, lines, rectangles, and circles such as LOGO, BASIC, Pascal, or C. (**Note:** Applesoft BASIC used with an Apple II computer cannot display text on the high- or low-resolution graphic screen and does not contain either a rectangle or a circle statement.) Graph paper containing the coordinates of the graphic page you plan to use. A printer (color is optional).

Procedure: After completing the first two programming activities, your students are ready to use their programming skill to draw a picture of a computer system. Each group needs to sketch their system before entering the code.

Evaluation: Evaluate students on the design and completion of their project and how the group cooperates as a team.

Special Tips: Be sure to check each group's sketch before students start entering the code. This is a perfect time to make comments on each group's work.

Mention to your students that they can create curves by drawing small connecting lines. This can become tedious, but the results are worth the effort.

Write a slide show program that displays all completed projects to share with current and future classes. You can do this by adding a hesitation loop followed by a line that calls the next project at the end of each program.

Display printouts of projects on a bulletin board for all students to see. Printing graphics is a slow process on a dot matrix printer. Have a printout sign-up sheet, and show one member from each group how to get a printout of their picture.

Groups can present their projects on a large-screen monitor in front of the class, or they can display their project on their computer, with each group floating around the room to view all the projects.

Name _____ Date _____

The Top-of-the-Line Computer

Using programming skills, draw a picture of a computer similar to the one shown below. The final picture should cover as much of the screen as possible. Feel free to make any changes or additions to the computer image. For example, you might want to put a graphic design or name for your group on the monitor. How about adding a second diskette drive, a second CD-ROM drive, an external modem, or even a keyboard? And don't leave out color. Decide which colors will make your computer stand out from the rest.

Begin by sketching your computer system on graph paper. Make sure your teacher sees your sketch before you start to enter the lines of code. Once your group has completed the project, you will have the opportunity to show it to the entire class.

So start sketching and get ready to program one top-of-the-line computer system.

45. Drawing Graphic Patterns with Loop Structures

Skills: **Programming**—writing a small graphic program with simple loop structures including the step function, drawing lines, and reading coordinates from graph paper.

Objectives: To write programs that contain a loop structure. To draw simple designs in the graphic environment of a programming language. To use small-group cooperative learning in computer programming.

Level: Intermediate.

Time Required: Two class periods.

Group Size: Three or more students.

Materials Needed: One computer per group. A programming language that can draw lines such as LOGO, BASIC, Pascal, or C. Graph paper containing the coordinates of the graphic page you plan to use.

Demonstrations Needed: Show how a hesitation loop can be used within a loop to slow down the graphic output. Here is a sample hesitation loop that can be used in BASIC:

FOR HES = 1 TO 1000 : NEXT HES.

Procedure: Each group spends time experimenting with loop structures and the graphic line statement by drawing six given graphic patterns. Your signature is required on each completed pattern. Each pattern can be drawn using one loop structure and one line statement within the loop. A challenge exercise is given for those groups that finish early.

Evaluation: Evaluate students on the number of graphic designs completed and how the group cooperates as a team.

Special Tips: Your students must be introduced to loop structures before starting this activity. For group practice, create a few sample exercises that include how each part of the loop works. Show students how to make a loop count forward and backward and how to increase or decrease the counters (steps).

Allow groups to share any new patterns with other groups.

Include all the patterns in one large program. After one pattern is complete, have each group include a hesitation loop followed by a command to clear the screen. The program can end with the last graphic pattern remaining on the screen. When all the graphics are completed, you can view each group's slide show for an approval signature.

Name _____ Date _____

Drawing Graphic Patterns with Loop Structures

Have you ever noticed some wild graphic patterns displayed on computer screens? While you might think it would take a long and complicated program to produce such an outstanding result, it really doesn't. With the use of loop structures and some algebraic manipulation, you can create all sorts of graphic patterns.

Look at the six triangular patterns below. It is up to your group to complete each one. You can draw each pattern with one loop structure and one line statement placed within the loop. The last three patterns require the step function of the loop to change from one to another number. So start experimenting with loop structures. You might even come up with some of your own wild graphic patterns. As you complete a pattern, show the screen output to your teacher for an approval signature, and then save the program to a disk under a unique file name.

Challenge: Program a loop to fill the screen with the color white by drawing horizontal lines down the screen. Then program another loop to draw a triangle pattern with black lines, stepping by two across the bottom of the screen. You should see an intriguing design when this is done.

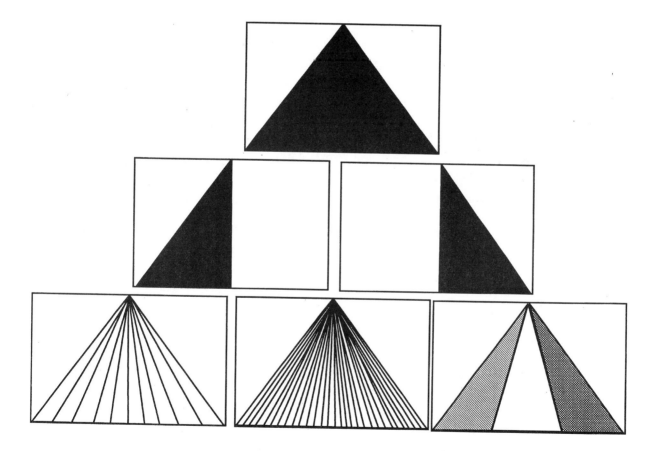

46. Loop Designs and Random Patterns

Skills: **Programming**—writing a small graphic program with simple loop structures including the step function, creating a random pattern, drawing points and lines, and reading coordinates from graph paper.

Objectives: To write programs that contain a loop structure. To draw simple designs in the graphic environment of a programming language. To create programs that generate a specific random graphic pattern within a loop structure. To use small-group cooperative learning in a programming setting.

Level: Intermediate.

Time Required: Two class periods.

Group Size: Three or more students.

Materials Needed: One computer per group. A programming language that can draw points and lines such as LOGO, BASIC, Pascal, or C. Graph paper containing the coordinates of the graphic page you plan to use.

Demonstrations Needed: Show how a hesitation loop can be used within a loop to slow down the graphic output. Here is a sample hesitation loop that can be used in BASIC:

FOR HES = 1 TO 1000 : NEXT HES.

Procedure: Each group uses loop structures to produce six given graphic patterns, four of which require the random statement to generate random graphic patterns. You sign each completed pattern. This activity is fun; each group can spend additional time creating a variety of patterns to share with other groups and classes.

Evaluation: Evaluate students on the number of graphic designs completed and how the group cooperates as a team.

Special Tips: Your students must be introduced to loop structures before starting this activity. For group practice, create a few sample exercises that include how each part of the loop works. Show students how to make a loop count forward and backward and how to increase or decrease the counters (steps).

Give each group a few examples of how the random statement works. Mention that the random statement can be used to assign coordinates to the point and line statements. The range of each random statement can be set to the length and width of the screen or to specific ranges where the pattern will appear. Promote the use of random colors with each design.

Allow groups to share any new patterns with other groups.

Include all the patterns in one large program, as in Activity 45.

Loop Designs and Random Patterns

You can use loop structures to create all kinds of graphic patterns. When you include a random statement with the loop, you can create patterns that are different every time you run the program. Your group is going to use loop structures to create the six graphic patterns shown below.

The first two do not need random statements; but the second pattern, which looks like a tic-tac-toe design, can be a little tricky. For this pattern, you might want to think about using more than one loop, with each loop containing two line statements. The remaining four patterns are generated by using one or more random statements placed within a loop structure. Each random statement can assign a numeric value to a variable used in a point or line statement. Feel free to set the number of random points and lines to any number you like. Start out with 100 and work from there. If you have time, try adding random color to each design, including the first two patterns.

As you complete a pattern, show the screen output to your teacher for an approval signature, and then save the program to a disk under a unique file name.

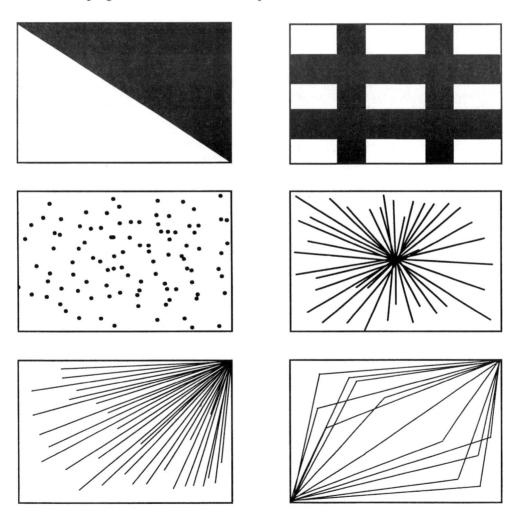

47. A Computer Slide Show

Skills: **Programming**—writing a large graphic program with simple loop structures including the step function, creating a random pattern, writing hesitation loops, drawing (points, lines, rectangles, and circles), and reading coordinates from graph paper.

Objectives: To write a more complex program that displays a series of graphic designs generated from within a loop structure. To create a graphic computer system where each design appears inside the monitor of the computer graphic. To use small-group cooperative learning in a programming setting.

Level: Intermediate.

Time Required: Three class periods.

Group Size: Three or more students.

Materials Needed: One computer per group. A programming language that can draw points and lines such as LOGO, BASIC, Pascal, or C. (**Note:** Applesoft BASIC used with an Apple II computer does not contain either a rectangle or a circle statement.) Graph paper containing the coordinates of the graphic page you plan to use.

Demonstrations Needed: Show how a hesitation loop can be used within a loop to slow down the graphic output. Here is a sample hesitation loop that can be used in **BASIC:**

FOR HES = 1 TO 1000 : NEXT HES.

Procedure: Your students apply all their programming skills to create a graphic slide show. Each group draws a picture of a computer and generates 10 to 15 graphic slides within their drawn computer's monitor. Students must use loop structures and a specified number of random patterns and colors. Each slide must remain on the screen for approximately two seconds and then be erased without erasing the picture of the computer. This challenging project will produce some outstanding results. All completed projects are presented to the class and handed in to you for grading.

Evaluation: Evaluate students on the design and completion of their project and how the group cooperates as a team.

Special Tips: Write a slide show program that displays all completed projects to share with current and future classes, as in Activity 44.

Students should have some background in programming graphic statements, simple loop structures, and random statements.

To save time, the drawing of the computer can be optional. Each graphic pattern can be displayed over the entire screen rather than within the drawn monitor.

A Computer Slide Show

Now your group has the opportunity to create your very own slide show. Your job is to write a program that displays a picture of a computer and, within the monitor of the computer, generates 10 to 15 different graphic patterns. Five of the graphic patterns must be randomly generated, and any three pictures must be generated in random colors. You must create seven of the patterns with a loop structure. Therefore, you can create other designs, like a logo or popular symbol, without using a loop structure or random statement.

Feel free to use a hesitation loop to slow down the run of each slide. Also, use a hesitation loop at the end of each slide's display to delay for approximately two seconds. Following this delay, you must erase the graphic from the monitor without erasing the picture of the computer. (**Hint:** Use a loop structure with a hesitation loop for an interesting effect, or simply draw a rectangle in the color of the background.)

Spend some time deciding what the computer will look like, the type of patterns that will create the slide show, and the order of slides. Will you save the best for last or show them off right away? Get some printouts of programs you might have written previously that you could add to this project.

When the project is completed, you will present it to the class and hand it in to your teacher for grading. Good luck; be creative and have fun!

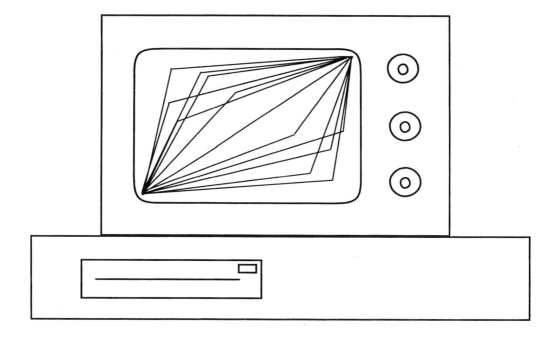

48. Password Protection

Skills: **Programming**—writing a small text-based program, inputting data from the user, comparing input using a conditional statement, and using a counter, a branching statement, and a conditional statement or a loop structure that allows a maximum of three inputs. (Optional: writing graphic statements to draw points, lines, rectangles, or circles.)

Objectives: To write a password protection program using group participation that allows the user only three chances to enter the correct password.

Level: Advanced.

Time Required: Two class periods.

Group Size: Three or more students.

Materials Needed: One computer per group. A programming language that can draw points and lines such as LOGO, BASIC, Pascal, or C. (**Note:** Applesoft BASIC used with an Apple II computer cannot display text on the high- or low-resolution graphic screens and does not contain either a rectangle or a circle statement.) Graph paper containing the coordinates of the graphic page you plan to use.

Procedure: Each group writes their own password protection program, using an input and a conditional statement. Comments, along with optional graphics and sounds, respond to the user's input. The program ends when the user enters the correct password or has entered three incorrect passwords.

Evaluation: Evaluate students on the design and completion of their project and how the group cooperates as a team.

Special Tips: Write a slide show program that displays all completed projects to share with current and future classes. You can do this by adding a hesitation loop followed by a line that calls up the next project at the end of each program.

Students should be familiar with using a condition statement that contains the "or" function. It will be needed to test for uppercase and lowercase input. Students can use separate conditional statements in place of one long statement containing the "or" function.

Students should be familiar with input statements. String variables are needed to accept text- or character-based input from the keyboard.

Upon completion, have each group use each other's program as a test.

To save time, do not require any graphics or sounds. Each group will then be able to complete the assignment in less than one period.

Password Protection

Has this happened to you? You try to log in to a computer but are blocked because of password protection. Imagine going on-line with your modem and surfing the 'Net (Internet) without passwords. It can't be done. All large computer systems and even some classroom networks require a user to enter an invisible password before being allowed access to the computer programs stored on the system. We all need this type of protection so our documents are not damaged by some other user. Imagine almost completing your term paper and then coming in the next day and finding that it is gone!

So passwords are used all over the computer world. Now your group's job is to write a password protection program that will allow the user only three attempts at logging in to your computer. After the third incorrect attempt, write a comment that denies the user access to your computer. For example, you could tell the user to get away from your computer or say you are calling security for help.

Test to make sure the program works for all situations. Accept the password in all uppercase or all lowercase letters. Feel free to add graphics, sounds, and color to your program. A wild graphic display for those getting into your system could be fun. Present your group's completed project to the class, and then hand it in to your teacher for grading.

49. State Trivia

Skills: **Programming**—writing a small text- and graphic-based program, allowing input from the user, comparing input using a conditional statement, creating a counter to track the number of correct and incorrect responses, drawing a picture on the graphic screen, and reading coordinates from graph paper.

Objectives: To write a graphic program that displays the image of one state in the United States. To ask the user to answer four multiple-choice questions and tally the number of correct and incorrect responses. To use small-group cooperative learning skills in a programming environment.

Level: Advanced.

Time Required: Three class periods.

Group Size: Three or more students.

Materials Needed: One computer per group. A programming language that can draw points and lines such as LOGO, BASIC, Pascal, or C. (**Note:** Applesoft BASIC used with an Apple II computer cannot display text on the high- or low-resolution graphic screens and does not contain either a rectangle or a circle statement.) Graph paper containing the coordinates of the graphic page you plan to use.

Procedure: Many U.S. trivia programs are on the market today. Now your class will create their own. You assign a different state to each group. The group draws a picture of the state and presents four multiple-choice questions about the state to the user.

Each program accepts user input. Counters keep track of the number of correct and incorrect answers. The correct answer is displayed when an incorrect answer is entered. Groups present their completed program to the class, and you grade it.

Evaluation: Evaluate students on the design and completion of their project and how the group cooperates as a team.

Special Tips: Write a slide show program that displays all completed projects to share with current and future classes, as in Activity 44.

Students should be familiar with using a condition statement that contains the "or" function. It will be needed to test for uppercase and lowercase input. Students can use separate conditional statements in place of one long statement containing the "or" function.

Students should be familiar with input statements. String variables are needed to accept text- or character-based input from the keyboard.

Upon completion, have each group use each other's program as a test.

You could assign more than one state to each group.

Have students use CD-ROM or reference software to research state trivia.

Name _____ Date _____

State Trivia

Now your group is going to apply your programming skills to create a state trivia game. Below is a list of the minimum requirements for this assignment. You will present your completed project to the class and then submit it for grading by your teacher.

The state trivia game must include:

- a picture of one state of the United States (no groups can have the same state)
- three trivia facts about the state (capital, famous river, nickname, etc.)
- four questions about the state in multiple-choice format displayed to the user one at a time
- counters that keep track of the number of correct and incorrect answers
- a display of a correct answer when an incorrect answer is entered
- a request for the user to enter her or his name
- acceptance of answers in uppercase or lowercase letters

50. The Quest for the Ultimate Adventure Game

Skills: **Programming**—designing a flowchart that outlines the flow of an adventure program, writing a large text- and graphic-based program from a predestined flowchart, allowing input from the user, comparing input using a conditional statement, drawing pictures on the graphic screen, reading coordinates from graph paper, and printing out a program list.

Objectives: To create a flowchart of a text and graphic adventure game. To write a computer program from a flowchart that contains at least ten different questions and five different areas to branch to. To use small-group cooperative learning skills in a programming environment.

Level: Advanced.

Time Required: Five class periods.

Group Size: Three or more students.

Materials Needed: One computer per group. A programming language that can draw points and lines such as LOGO, BASIC, Pascal, or C. (**Note:** Applesoft BASIC used with an Apple II computer cannot display text on the high- or low-resolution graphic screen and does not contain either a rectangle or a circle statement.) Graph paper containing the coordinates of the graphic page you plan to use.

Procedure: Groups use all their programming skills to write a text- and graphic-based adventure program. Each group starts by creating a complete flowchart of the game and gives it to you for approval. The programs written must follow the flowchart. Each project must contain an opening and closing graphic screen along with a description of the game at the beginning. The game must include ten different questions and five different areas for the user to enter.

Evaluation: Evaluate students on the design and completion of their project and how the group cooperates as a team.

Special Tips: Insist on each group's making plenty of printouts throughout the project. These printouts are helpful in case someone damages the file or accidentally erases it. Require the group to bring you the latest printout when asking for your help in debugging the program.

Make sure all programs are backed up on two or more disks. Have a disk of your own that students use for backup, so that you have the latest version of the program.

Give students time to test their project and debug mistakes.

Introduce subroutines or procedures, which are helpful because adventure games allow the user to return to a given setting. Graphic scenes can easily be located in a subroutine or procedure and therefore can be called up from just about anywhere in the program.

You can run this activity over a long period of time, allowing groups to get together once or twice a week to work on the project.

The Quest for the Ultimate Adventure Game

You probably have played a computer adventure game, like one in the King's Quest series. In these games, you have to make decision after decision and continually search for clues that will lead you in the right direction. Most of the games today contain video clips, beautiful pictures, paintings, and just a little text information. However, not so long ago, the major section of an adventure game was text with a few graphics. Now, your group is about to create your very own adventure game. Will it contain a lot of graphics and sounds? Will it contain thought-provoking text that leads the user through a maze of excitement?

This is a long and challenging project; but as a team, you will surely produce a creative adventure that all students in your school will enjoy playing. Organization and following through with the original flowchart are the keys to success in this project. Here are the minimum requirements for the project:

- Create a complete flowchart before writing the code and show it to your teacher for approval.

- Add graphics and color.

- Try to use subroutines or procedures that display repeating screens. This often happens when the user returns to a previous section of the game.

- Include an opening graphic screen and a closing graphic screen.

- Include a description of the adventure at the beginning of the game.

- Ask for the user's first name, and use it throughout the game.

- Ask at least 10 questions in the course of the game.

- Have the program branch to at least five different sections of the program.

  Here are a couple of optional ideas:

- Add sounds.

- Add animation.

CHAPTER 8

Telecommunications

51. Global Keyboard Pals

Skills: **Word Processing**—starting a new document, editing, spell checking, performing block operations, saving and opening a file, saving a file in text or ASCII format, and printing.

Objectives: To become familiar with telecommunication by using electronic mail. To use small-group cooperation to communicate with and learn about other students in another part of the world.

Level: Beginning.

Group Size: Three to four students.

Time Required: Periodic activity. This is a good activity for groups to do during free time.

Materials Needed: One computer with word processing capabilities per group. You need access to a modem and a bulletin board service or the Internet to send and receive the e-mail.

Demonstrations Needed: Once you have established a communication link with another school and classroom, demonstrate to the students how this was done.

Procedure: Groups of students compose letters and then use electronic mail to send their messages to another class somewhere in the world. First you will need to spend some time on-line searching for another classroom and school willing to make e-mail exchanges. Once you have established a link, your students compose a list of questions for their new friends. After the questions are sent, answered, and returned, have the cooperative-learning groups present their findings to the class.

Evaluation: Evaluate students based on small-group interaction, letter-writing skills, the list of questions, and the final presentation.

Special Tips: Have a separate disk available for all groups on which to save their completed e-mail. Compress all the files (referred to as zipping) into one file before sending, and have your long-distance co-teacher do the same. Decompress the received e-mail file (referred to as *unzipping*) into many text documents. Demonstrate to the class how zipping and unzipping are done.

E-mail must be saved in a text, or ASCII, format. Show students how to export a word processing file to text or ASCII, and to format and import their mail into their word processor.

Make sure your on-line service allows you to attach a file to an e-mail document. (America Online does.) This feature allows you to send scanned images of your class along with any type of document. Check to make sure the teacher receiving the e-mail has the correct software to read the files.

Global Keyboard Pals

Sometimes it is easier to meet people when you are in a group setting. In this activity, meeting new people will be a breeze! Today, millions of computer users are writing letters to each other electronically. As long as two computers each have a modem connected to a phone line, the users can communicate. In the computer world, this form of writing letters is known as "e-mail," or electronic mail. It's fast, inexpensive, and fun!

Your teacher has already made contact with a teacher at another school somewhere in the world. Your keyboard pals attend this school, and your job is to find out interesting information about where they live. You may be communicating with students from another state or even another country.

Each group must write one opening letter to your keyboard friends. Using a word processor, tell them a little about yourselves and your school. On a separate page, write a list of *at least 15 questions* for the other group to answer. Here is a list of questions you can use, if you wish, to help you get started:

- What does your school look like?

- How long is your school day?

- What do you eat for lunch at your school?

- How large is your city or town?

- What are the interesting things to do in your city or town?

After you have written your introductory letter and list of questions, print it out and proofread it carefully. Make any updates, print a final copy, and show it to your teacher. Once your teacher has approved the letter, save the word processing document on your data disk and the teacher's class disk. Using telecommunications technology, your teacher will combine all the documents into one file and send all the class letters and lists through the computer, through the modem, through the phone lines, to the other students' classroom computer.

Waiting for the reply is the most difficult part of this activity. While it only takes a minute or two for your e-mail to arrive at its destination, it could take some time to receive e-mail back. Depending on language barriers and computer access time, it could take anywhere from a few days to over a week for the other class to reply to your mail. Be patient! When you finally receive your reply, read it as a group. Did they answer all your questions? And do they have questions for you?

The polite thing to do is to reply to their letter. Do so as a group. Answer all their questions to the best of your ability. You never know—you might just keep in touch with each other through the entire school year.

52. Weather-wise

Skills: **Telecommunications**—logging in to a bulletin board system, displaying weather maps, and downloading maps and text information to a classroom computer.

Objectives: To practice telecommunication skills through the use of a bulletin board service. To work together as a group to report the weather.

Level: Intermediate.

Time Required: One class period for all the students to familiarize themselves with the bulletin board service and its weather service. Each group gives a weather report for one whole week at the *end* of each class. The actual report should not take more than five minutes; however, the reporting group will need extra time to prepare.

Group Size: Three to six students. Five is the ideal number so that each student in the group is required to report the weather during a week's time.

Materials Needed: One computer with a modem connection to an on-line bulletin board service per group. A network modem connection would be ideal. The students could download the pertinent maps and display them on all the screens.

Maps could also be displayed on a large monitor. If you do not have this technology, make sure the students have access to a printer and conventional drawing materials.

Procedure: Each group reports the weather for one week. The "acting meteorologists" use the last five minutes of each class period to present weather predictions. Students use a bulletin board service to collect information and download maps.

Evaluation: Evaluate students based on group interaction and final presentation. Note that on some days, students may be rushed to present their reports. Take this into consideration.

Special Tips: If you do not have access to a bulletin board service, students can use daily newspapers as a source of weather information, or you could make this activity a homework assignment, with students watching a weather report on television.

Set aside bulletin board space for daily printouts. Students can watch the weather pattern for the week, as it appears on the bulletin board.

Weather-wise

In this activity, your group acts as meteorologists. Yes, you are going to forecast the weather. Everyone always gives meteorologists such a hard time when their predictions are wrong. Now it is your turn to be in the hot seat! Each group is going to forecast the weather every day for one week.

Before you start talking about cold fronts and thunderstorms, familiarize yourselves with the tools you are going to use to help predict the weather. Every major bulletin board service (BBS) such as America Online, Prodigy, and CompuServe has weather information for its members to use. Your job, as a group, is to retrieve that information, forecast the weather, and share your forecast with the rest of the class.

Your teacher will tell you well in advance during which coming week your group is responsible for reporting the weather. Today, you may want to try a practice run and/or prepare some of your visual aids ahead of time. Here are a few things you may wish to include in your report:

- national map
- state map
- regional map
- today's current weather data

- tonight's forecast
- tomorrow's forecast
- three-day outlook forecast

Visual aids are very important when it comes to reporting the weather. You can create your maps and other data charts in a number of ways. First, you could simply download the maps directly from the BBS. Second, you could use geography or drawing/painting software to create your own maps. Or third, if you do not have the technology, use a daily newspaper to collect the information, and use conventional drawing materials to create your visual aids.

When your week arrives, your teacher will tell you how much class time you have to prepare your report. Some days you will have more time than others. Your teacher is well aware of this fact and will take time allowances into consideration when assigning grades. You will present your weather report during the last five minutes of class. Each member of the group is required to present some information at one time or another. Try to divide the work evenly, both the researching and the reporting. Good luck, and don't forget your umbrella!

53. Schoolhouse News

Skills: (1) **Telecommunications**—logging in to a bulletin board system and downloading text information to a computer in the classroom.
(2) **Word Processing**—starting a new document, editing, spell checking, performing block operations, saving and opening a file, and printing.
(3) **Drawing/Painting** and/or **Stationery** software—creating visual aids.

Objectives: To use a bulletin board service, the Internet, and school resources to present a simulated news broadcast, working in a small-group setting.

Level: Advanced.

Group Size: Three to six students.

Time Required: Preparation time may take anywhere from three to five class periods. Assign one or two groups per class period for the actual broadcasts.

Materials Needed: One computer with a modem connected to an on-line bulletin board service and possibly the Internet for each group; lacking this, conventional research resources. Access to multimedia and draw/paint software (helpful for creating visual aids). Word processing software and a printer.

Procedure: Students present a simulated television news broadcast, collecting their information from a bulletin board service and possibly the Internet and school resources. Then, they work on the broadcast, dividing their presentation into logical categories much like a real broadcast. Visual aids are required. The actual broadcasts should last anywhere from 15 to 20 minutes.

Evaluation: Evaluate students based on information-collecting skills, group interaction, and the final broadcast.

Special Tips: This is an advanced exercise. Students should have previous experience working with BBS, the Internet, multimedia, and drawing/painting software.

Inform the students that by the time they perform their broadcasts, their news may be out-of-date. This is understandable and will not affect their grade.

You will be surprised what some of your students will come up with for this activity. Some students will use music, bring in "real people" to interview, create commercials, etc. All of these additions are fun and interesting. Encourage them whenever possible.

Make the broadcasts seem more real by recording them with a camcorder. During free time, play back the broadcasts. Students love to see themselves on TV.

Name _____ Date _____

Schoolhouse News

"Good afternoon, and welcome to Westside Junior High School's Channel 10 News."

Soon, words similar to these will sound familiar to you. In this activity, your group will produce and present a simulated television news broadcast.

Putting together a news broadcast takes a great deal of organization. Before digging into the vast amount of information and news, decide what you are looking for. Divide your group into areas of interest. Some of the major areas of a news broadcast are as follows:

- international news
- state news
- school news
- weather
- investigative reporting
- consumer news

- national news
- local news
- sports (professional, college, your school)
- entertainment news
- health news
- interviews

Once you have chosen your areas of interest and assigned the work accordingly, start your research. Use your bulletin board service and possibly the Internet. Download interesting articles or use your word processing software to take notes. Return to the group, and discuss the news stories you wish to present. As a group, decide which stories to use and which ones to drop.

Visual aids are a very important part of any television broadcast. Your group is required to have at least *five* visuals in your broadcast. You can create them in a number of ways. Use multi-media software and present all your visuals on a monitor. Use drawing/painting and stationery software to create them. As a last resort, create them by hand. Everyone in the group is required to help with the visual aids.

Now that you have the news items and visuals, start practicing the simulated broadcast. News broadcasters practice reading the articles over and over. Not only does practice create a polished performance, it also makes the broadcaster feel more comfortable. Practice with each other, giving helpful hints for improvement as well as positive praise. Everyone in the group is required to do some of the broadcasting. Practice will also tell you the length of broadcast. It should be at least 15 minutes long.

Your teacher will assign your group a performance day. Your audience will be your class-mates. On that day, you may wish to dress as broadcasters do. As a group, make sure everything is organized and ready to go.

Good luck! Five, four, three, two, one, *action*!

CHAPTER 9

Multimedia
Presentation
Software

54. Who's Who Slide Show

Skills: (1) **Scanner**—scanning a photo into the computer and saving it in a graphic format that can be imported into a multimedia presentation program or a drawing/painting program. (2) **Multimedia Presentation Program** (hypertext, hypermedia program)—importing scanned images, adding text frames to pages, and adding clickable buttons that allow users to move between pages.

Objectives: To expose students to multimedia presentation software and the use of a scanner. To present a graphic slide show within a small-group setting.

Level: Beginning.

Group: Three to six students.

Time Required: Two to three days. If you only have one scanner, the groups will have to take turns. This may increase the amount of time needed to complete this activity.

Materials Needed: One computer per group with multimedia presentation software or a graphic viewing program. A scanner.

Procedure: Students love this activity. Not only do they get to look at old pictures of themselves, they also get to look at old pictures of each other. This is a great way to expose students to multimedia software and the use of a scanner. Each group scans in three pictures of each group member. With each picture, they include some text in the form of a hint and a unique identification number. The group then presents their slide show to their classmates. The rest of the class attempts to identify the person in each multimedia slide by writing down a student's name and the slide's identification number on a piece of paper. The group that stumps the most students wins!

Demonstrations Needed: A demonstration of using scanning and multimedia presentation software usage is highly recommended. The students would love it if you scanned in one of *your* old baby pictures. In addition, demonstrate how to include text with a scanned image. If time permits, show students how to edit a scanned image by cleaning up any flaws that occurred during the scan or by removing sections of the image that are not wanted.

Evaluation: Evaluate students based on group participation and the quality of their slide show, including the text.

Special Tips: The use of multimedia presentation software is optional. Scanned images can be saved as graphic files and worked on in a painting program. Students can simply load in the files one at a time during the presentation to the class or randomly run all of the graphics with a special viewing program. An excellent viewing program for PC computers is VuePrint. It can be found on most bulletin board services and can be downloaded to preview.

Suggested multimedia presentation programs that can be used for this activity include: HyperCard for the Macintosh and Linkway for the PC.

Make sure the students put their names on the back of the original picture. Losing old pictures is a tragedy parents won't appreciate.

Different classes or grades could present their slide shows to each other.

Ask another teacher, or even the principal, to come in and try to guess the identity of the students in the slide show. Kids love to see teachers or a principal squirm!

A slide show is a wonderful demonstration of technology to present to parents during parent/teacher conferences, festivals, or fairs.

If you do not have a scanner, have students make creative frames on the computers that each picture can be displayed in. Tape all of the framed pictures on a large piece of colored paper before presenting to the class.

Who's Who Slide Show

What did you look like as a baby? Did you have curly hair, black hair, or no hair at all? What did you look like as a toddler? Did you have chubby cheeks, a pot belly, or beanpole legs? What did you look like in first grade? Did you have a wild haircut, stylish clothes, or a missing front tooth?

Some of these questions may be answered in this multimedia activity. As a group, you will present a slide show of your old pictures to the rest of the class. The class will try to identify the person in every photograph. Will they be able to guess who's who? The object of the activity is to stump the rest of the class, so pick those unusual pictures of yourselves.

Every student's assignment is to bring *at least five* old pictures to class. As a group, decide which *three* pictures from the five look the *least* like your teammate. Once you have chosen three pictures per group member, get the computer scanner out. Make sure the proper multimedia software is up and running. Scan in all the chosen pictures.

To make it a little easier on your classmates, include a hint about the person in the picture. Don't make the hint too obvious; you don't want to give away the correct choice on the text alone. Once you have the pictures and text prepared, attach a number to each of the slides. Make the number large enough to be seen by viewers from a slight distance away. In addition, mix up the order in which the pictures appear; don't have all three of one group member's pictures clumped together.

If you are using a multimedia presentation program, be sure to include selectable buttons (usually arrows) that allow the user to move back and forth between slides. If you are presenting the pictures with a viewing program, take advantage of any of the built-in features that will enliven your show. For example, most viewing programs allow you automatically to display the pictures in random order for a given period of time. Use as many of the available features as possible.

Now it is time for the "Who's Who Slide Show." Each group takes a turn presenting their show. The rest of the class tries to guess who is in each picture; each person writes down the identifying number on a sheet of paper and makes a guess by writing down a classmate's name. The class may ask to review the slide show *once*. After your presentation is complete, reveal the answers to the rest of the class. Have your classmates count up how many answers they got *wrong*. The slide show group that stumped the most people wins!

55. Authors and Illustrators

Skills: (1) **Multimedia Presentation Program** (hypertext, hypermedia program)—importing graphic files (painting, clip art), adding text frames to pages, adding clickable buttons that allow users to move between pages, and importing sound files and video clips (optional). (2) **Drawing/Painting**—Painting tools include: line, spray paint, polygon, box, rounded box, ellipse, curve, and fill. Editing tools include: zoom, eraser, color eraser, and the undo command. Block operations include: copy, move, shrink and grow, tilt, flip, rotate, and inverse, and importing clip art pictures.

Objectives: To create a children's story through the use of drawing/painting software and multimedia presentation software within a frame of small-group interaction.

Level: Intermediate.

Time Required: Five class periods.

Group Size: Three to six students.

Materials Needed: At least one computer per group. With less than one computer per group, some students could write the text while others work on the illustrations.

Procedure: Most middle school students will never admit it, but they enjoy looking at children's storybooks. Here the students create a multimedia storybook of 10 to 15 pages plus a cover page. Using drawing/painting software, students create colorful illustrations and add color to imported clip art.

Students then save these illustrations and import them into the multimedia presentation program, where they are sized, positioned, and grouped together, and text is added. Classes of all ages will enjoy these storybooks.

Evaluation: Evaluate students based on group interaction and use of the multimedia presentation software.

Special Tips: Have each group create an outline, which you must approve, before starting work on the computer. Each group must then follow the outline without any major changes.

This would be an excellent activity to co-teach with the English and/or art teacher.

Try to arrange a showing of your student's multimedia storybooks to elementary school-aged children. Try contacting the technology teacher in the elementary school.

Emphasize the use of sound. Students often forget this helpful and entertaining attribute of multimedia. Some music departments have computers with music cards that allow music to be recorded in a format compatible with most multimedia presentations. A student can play an instrument while the computer writes the music to file.

In cooperation with the social studies or English teacher, have the students create a storybook about one of the historical characters they are studying in another class.

Authors and Illustrators

Have you ever wondered what it would be like to be an author or illustrator? You are going to find out. In this activity, your group will write and illustrate a multimedia children's book.

The first step in creating a multimedia storybook is to invent a character or characters who will appear in your book. As a group, discuss whom and what you believe little kids would enjoy reading about. How about a dinosaur or a gorilla or a train or a flying vegetable? Remember, you will also be illustrating this story; do not pick something that is too difficult to draw.

Once you have chosen a character, the story line is the next step. Almost all stories contain some kind of conflict. Maybe a baby dinosaur gets lost, or maybe a gorilla is captured by a mean hunter, or maybe a toy train rescues a little boy, or a flying vegetable saves the world. Conflict makes a story interesting—even a children's story.

When your group has a basic story line in mind, start writing and illustrating. Here are the requirements you must meet:

1. The story must be *at least 300* words in length and between *10 and 15* pages long.

2. The story must include one illustration per page. Each illustration can be made up of clip art pictures and paintings.

3. The children's story must have a book cover including the title, authors, and illustrators. As with a traditional book cover, you may want to include an illustration.

Create your illustrations by using a drawing/painting program. Add colors to clip art pictures by importing them into a drawing/painting program. You can break an illustration into sections and put it together in the multimedia presentation program. For example, one member of the group can work on a clip art picture while another member uses a painting program to draw a background scene. The two pictures can be imported separately into the multimedia presentation program, overlapped, resized, and grouped together.

While using the multimedia presentation program, be sure to include selectable buttons (usually arrows) that allow users to move back and forth between slides. Check to see if any sound files or animated clips came with the program. If so, use whichever ones will complement your story. If you have access to a modem, try downloading a few sound files; you can choose from thousands of free ones. You might even find a few animated clips.

Once you have finished your multimedia storybook, all of you are officially authors and/or illustrators. Congratulations! Present your multimedia storybook to the rest of the class. And if at all possible, present your storybooks to the intended audience—little kids.

56. Multimedia Time Capsule

Skills: (1) **Multimedia Presentation Program** (hypertext, hypermedia program)—importing graphic files (painting, clip art), adding text frames to pages, adding clickable buttons that allow the users to move between pages, and importing sound files and video clips (optional). (2) **Research**—CD-ROM (optional), telecommunication (optional), and book references.

Objectives: To use multimedia software and small-group cooperative learning to create a time capsule.

Level: Intermediate.

Time Required: Four class periods.

Group Size: Three to six students.

Materials Needed: At least one computer with multimedia capabilities per group. More than one computer would be useful; some students could collect information and others could work on the presentation. CD-ROM, bulletin board services, and Internet access would also be helpful.

Procedure: Students put together a class multimedia time capsule. Each small group chooses, researches, and presents one subject area of interest. The student page gives suggestions, but new ideas are encouraged. Each group presents their completed time capsule to the rest of the class. Volunteers combine all the sections.

Evaluation: Evaluate students based on group interaction, research-gathering skills, multimedia presentation software use, and the final presentation.

Special Tips: Make sure one of the groups decides to do the personal profiles. Students love to see their faces and friends' faces on a monitor.

Emphasize the use of sound. Students often forget this helpful and entertaining attribute of multimedia. Some music departments have computers with music cards that allow music to be recorded in a format compatible with most multimedia presentations. A student can play an instrument while the computer writes the music to file.

Preserve these multimedia time capsules not only for future classes but also for the present classes themselves. These time capsules would be great to show at graduation dinner or a class reunion.

Multimedia Time Capsule

What will your school be like in 10 or even 20 years? When those future students are looking at old yearbooks—your yearbooks—what will they think of you? Will they laugh at your hairstyles? At your clothing styles? After all, what do you think of old pictures from the 1970's and 1980's? Do you ever wonder what those students were really like? Future students won't have to wonder about you. A time capsule will solve that problem.

In this activity, your class is going to put together a time capsule in a multimedia format for future students to open and investigate. Each small group is responsible for choosing and gathering information on one subject area. Here are some suggestions:

- personal profiles (a picture and paragraph about everyone in the class)

- hairstyles and clothing fashions

- popular music

- popular movies

- current events (international, national, school news)

- sports and entertainment (professional and school-related)

- popular games and activities

Once your group has chosen a subject area, start conducting research. Use your library's reference materials as well as your computer (CD-ROM encyclopedias, bulletin board services, Internet, etc.). You will preserve your time capsule in multimedia format. This allows for pictures, sound, and text to be saved on a disk and reopened 10 to 20 years from now. Use as much technology as possible. For example, you can include clip art, a painting, or even a chart generated from a spreadsheet. How about scanning pictures?

While using the multimedia presentation program, be sure to include selectable buttons (usually arrows) that allow users to move back and forth between slides. Check to see if any sound files or animated clips came with the program. If so, use whichever ones will complement your time capsule. If you have access to a modem, try downloading a few sound files or animated clips; you'll have plenty of free ones to choose from. While you're searching the bulletin boards, look for graphics files of people, places, and events that will go with your time capsule.

All projects will be presented to the class. As you watch the groups' presentations, pretend you are a student from the future. Do the presentations give you an accurate glimpse of this time period? Do you need to add anything important? If not, discuss with your teacher how the class is going to preserve the time capsule.

57. Group Travel Agency

Skills: (1) **Multimedia Presentation Program** (hypertext, hypermedia program)—importing graphic files (painting, clip art), adding text frames to pages, adding clickable buttons that allow users to move between pages, and importing sound files and video clips (optional). (2) **Research** CD-ROM (optional), telecommunication (optional), and book references.

Objectives: To use multimedia software to create a presentation on a travel destination. To use small group interaction to collect information and create a multimedia presentation.

Level: Advanced.

Time Required: Five class periods.

Group Size: Three to six students.

Materials Needed: At least one computer with multimedia capabilities per group. More than one computer would be useful; some students could collect information and others could work on the presentation. CD-ROM, bulletin board services, and Internet access would also be helpful.

Procedure: Students play the role of travel agents, creating a multimedia sales presentation about a chosen summer vacation destination. Each group uses conventional and high-tech means to collect information about their particular vacation spot and then uses multimedia software to create a sales pitch for the benefit of you, the teacher/customer. In the end, you choose where to go.

Evaluation: Evaluate students based on small-group participation, multimedia presentation software usage, and the final presentation.

Special Tips: It's helpful if you preapprove all the destinations. Warn the students about choosing too big or too small a subject.

Remind students of the advantages of using sound. They often forget about this aspect of multimedia.

In place of a multimedia presentation program, use existing programs on the market that contain all the pictures, sound, maps, and videos, like The Picture Atlas of the World by National Geographic. This excellent CD-ROM program allows students to create their own slide shows by selecting any text frame, picture, sound, map, or video and snapping it into a file that can be saved on a disk and presented to the class. Students can even type their own information into a text frame. Then simply load the student file and run the show. That's it! You can edit existing slides and insert or delete slides. These types of programs are easy to learn and allow students at all levels to create beautiful slide shows with all of the reference material built into one CD-ROM.

Group Travel Agency

In this activity, your group acts as a travel agency. Your best customer, your teacher, longs to travel to somewhere interesting. Your teacher plans to travel for eight weeks during summer vacation. Money is no object, because your teacher recently won the lottery. Booking this trip could bring a great deal of money into your newly formed travel agency business.

You will compete against other travel agencies (other groups in your class) for your customer's business. You must not only come up with a great place for your teacher to travel to, but also make an impressive presentation—you must sell your ideas and travel plans! Each group will make a multimedia sales pitch. Your teacher will decide where to go based on the ideas presented as well as the quality of the multimedia presentations themselves.

As a group, discuss and decide which travel destination you wish to promote. You also need to decide what type of vacation to promote. Will it be relaxing or adventurous, historical, romantic, or a combination? What do you believe your teacher would enjoy the most?

Once your group has the destination and type of vacation in mind, start researching. Remember, all information collected should be helpful in selling your destination to your customer. Ignore boring, useless facts. Collect interesting facts and information. Your customer needs to be able to make an educated decision.

Conduct your research by using regular reference materials as well as high-tech options such as CD-ROM software, bulletin board services, and the Internet. You can transfer or scan information into the multimedia software. Use as much technology as possible. For example, you can include clip art, a painting, or even a chart generated from a spreadsheet. How about scanning pictures?

While using the multimedia presentation program, be sure to include selectable buttons (usually arrows) that allow users to move back and forth between slides. Check to see if any sound files or animated clips came with the program. If so, use whichever ones will complement your project. If you have access to a modem, try downloading a few sound files or animated clips; you'll have plenty of free ones to choose from. While you're searching the bulletin boards, look for graphics files of people, places, and events that will go with your electronic travel guide.

Present your multimedia sales pitch to your customer as well as the other travel agencies. After all the travel agencies have made their sales presentations, your customer will make a decision. Good luck!

58. Student-Generated Multimedia Encyclopedia

Skills: (1) **Multimedia Presentation Program** (hypertext, hypermedia program)—importing graphic files (painting, clip art), adding text frames to pages, adding clickable buttons that allow users to move between pages, and importing sound files and video clips (optional).
(2) **Research**—CD-ROM (optional), telecommunication (optional), and book references.

Objectives: To use multimedia software to enhance text in an encyclopedia environment. To use small-group cooperative learning to create a student-generated multimedia encyclopedia.

Level: Advanced.

Time Required: Five class periods.

Group Size: Three to six students.

Materials Needed: One computer with multimedia capabilities per group. More than one computer per group would be helpful for collecting research and using drawing/painting and word processing software. CD-ROM, bulletin board services, and Internet access would also be helpful. Also needed: a scanner (optional) and a printer.

Procedure: Students add pictures and sound to create a multimedia encyclopedia. Students who completed the database exercise on creating an encyclopedia can use any of those existing records as part of their research. Students can use a number of different software programs to assist them with this activity, including word processing, drawing/painting, desktop publishing, and CD-ROM software, as well as bulletin board services and the Internet. Once the students have completed the multimedia entries, they present them to you and the rest of the class.

Evaluation: Evaluate students based on multimedia software usage, group participation, the final product, and its usefulness to other students.

Special Tips: Assign students who completed the database encyclopedia activity to the same group, and have each group convert their previous work into a multimedia format. This will save a lot of research time.

If your students have *not* completed the encyclopedia database activity, have them do the text research now. This will, of course, lengthen the time needed for this activity. In this situation, you can allow each group to choose a topic rather than assigning it to them.

As an extra-credit assignment, have a group of students create a table of contents page that allows users to access any of the projects completed by each group. As each class completes a new section, add it to this file. Before you know it, you will have your very own user-friendly multimedia encyclopedia.

Name _____ Date _____

Student-Generated Multimedia Encyclopedia

Imagine you are in the library researching the famous composer Ludwig van Beethoven. You open the *B* encyclopedia to "Beethoven," and all of a sudden you hear a symphony playing his music!

This could really happen to you if you were looking at a computer screen instead of a book. In fact, *you* could make this happen. In this activity, you will create a multimedia encyclopedia for you, yourself, and other students to use.

In the database chapter, you and your group may have completed on activity in which you created text entries for an encyclopedia. Now, in this activity, you add pictures, sounds, and text to a new multimedia encyclopedia. If you did complete the database activity, feel free to use any of its content with this new project. After your teacher has placed you in a group and assigned a subject area, start researching for text, graphic, and sound information. Not every entry has to include a graphic or sound.

Use your multimedia software to help you. Don't forget about other helpful software such as drawing/painting and CD-ROM programs. Let's say your subject is mammals and, more specifically, horses. You could draw a horse or go out and grab a photograph of a horse from CD-ROM software or simply import a picture of a horse from the clip art library. Let's not leave out the use of a scanner, either. Try to use as much technology as possible.

Enter all text information into a word processing document where it can be spell checked. Print, proofread, and update each document before importing it into the multimedia presentation program.

While using the multimedia presentation program, be sure to include selectable buttons (usually arrows) that allow users to move back and forth between slides. Check to see if any sound files or animated clips came with the program. If so, use whichever ones will complement your project. If you have access to a modem, try downloading a few sound files or animated clips; you'll have plenty of free ones to choose from. While you're searching the bulletin boards, look for graphics files of people, places, and events that will go with your multimedia encyclopedia.

Once you have completed adding multimedia aspects to your encyclopedia entries, show them to the rest of the class. Make sure that you save all your entries and that your entries can be easily accessed by other students, who may want to use your encyclopedia as a reference.

CHAPTER 10

Miscellaneous

59. Bulletin Board Contest

Skills: Word processing, desktop publishing, drawing/painting, and/or stationery software.

Objectives: To research, design, and create a bulletin board using computer technology and small-group interaction.

Level: Beginning.

Time Required: Three class periods.

Group Size: Three to six students.

Materials Needed: As many computers per group as possible. Students should have access to a wide variety of computer technology, including CD-ROM software, bulletin board services, the Internet, word processing, drawing/painting and desktop publishing software, and old computer magazines. Art supplies will also be needed.

Procedure: This activity may benefit you, the teacher, more than anyone else. Your students will decorate your room for you. As part of a contest, each cooperative learning group researches, designs, and creates a bulletin board. You must supply wall space for the students to display their work. An unbiased person of your choice chooses the best bulletin board, to be displayed outside the classroom.

Evaluation: Evaluate students based on research skills, the amount of technology used, group participation, and the bulletin board itself.

Special Tips: Because you have limited wall space, this activity can be done by only one class at a time.

If your art supplies are limited, remind students to bring in their own art supplies. The art teacher may be willing to work with you on this activity.

Encourage the students to use a wide variety of computer technology to assist them with this project. Remind them that part of their grade is based on technology use.

A great resource for discarded computer parts (chips, boards, disk drives, etc.) is your local computer store. Encourage students to visit a computer store, explain to the owner the project they are working on, and collect some of these old parts. Remind the students to ask questions about each part and to take good notes. They can polish up their notes later on the computer and display them on the bulletin board with each part.

Hang the hardware parts on the bulletin board by tying each with string and stapling the string to the board.

If you have access to a number of bulletin boards throughout the school, use all of them. The bulletin board that wins the contest should be displayed on the most prestigious space.

Bulletin Board Contest

Bare walls in any classroom are a shame, especially in a technology classroom. So many interesting subjects are tied to technology and computers! In this activity, you and your group will help your teacher decorate the classroom walls by creating a bulletin board. The best bulletin board will be displayed outside the classroom.

After your teacher has placed you in a group, discuss possible bulletin board ideas. Come up with your own subject, or use one of the following ideas:

- The Latest and Greatest in Computer Technology
- What Is the Internet and How Does It Work?
- Bill Gates—The Microsoft Giant
- Student Computer Projects on Display
- Advertisement for a New Software Package

- The History of Computers
- Educational Games
- Computer Art
- Technology in the News
- The Dos and Don'ts of PC Use

Once your group has chosen a subject, design the bulletin board. Use your drawing/painting, desktop publishing, or stationery software to help you lay out the bulletin board plan. Once you have a plan, divide the work evenly. Use as many aspects of computer technology as possible to help you with your bulletin board. For example, use CD-ROM software, bulletin board services, or the Internet to help you with your research. Use word processing, drawing/painting, desktop publishing, and stationery software to draw and write items to display. Cut out examples and articles from old computer magazines.

Your teacher will supply your group with as many art supplies as possible; however, do not depend on your teacher for *all* of the supplies. You may need to bring some items from home. Your teacher will, of course, supply you with the wall space. Display your bulletin board, keeping in mind that a bulletin board is a visual medium. Use appealing colors, lettering, and pictures.

After all the bulletin boards are up and on display, your teacher will bring in an unbiased party to decide which bulletin board should be displayed outside the room. Who will this unbiased person be—maybe the principal, another teacher, a secretary, the school nurse, the librarian, a school cook, or a school bus driver? Whoever it is, the decision stands. Good luck!

60. Fun with Fairs

Skills: Word processing, desktop publishing, drawing/painting, and/or stationery software use.

Objectives: To use small- and large-group cooperative techniques to create and operate a booth or booths at a school fair that will help promote and assist the technology program. To use cooperative learning techniques to brainstorm booth ideas.

Level: Intermediate.

Time Required: Two days for brainstorming, list making, decision making, and presenting the idea to the rest of the class. Time needed for the actual creation of products and/or booth will vary.

Group Size: Three to six students per initial group. Group size may or may not increase depending on the number of booths you wish to run.

Materials Needed: Varies with booth ideas.

Procedure: Almost every school during the year has a fair or carnival, parents' night, or student showcase. Students love to run booths at these events, and if they are educational, all the better. In this activity, small groups brainstorm to come up with technology-related booth ideas. A small list of ideas is provided to help the students get started. Once they have a list, they show it to you. Together, decide on the most appropriate and beneficial booth idea. The small group then presents the idea to the class. After all groups have made their presentations, the class votes on which booth or booths to use during the fair.

Evaluation: Evaluate students based on the group's idea list and presentation. You may wish to grade the students after the fair, but keep in mind that student effort may be outstanding even though a booth idea flops.

Special Tips: Some of the booth ideas will take a great deal of work, but some may already be completed. For example, if you have completed the calendar activity in the desktop publishing chapter of this book, you already have a product to sell.

During the fair, display as many additional class projects as you can. Run slide shows of computer painting or programming projects on stand-alone computers. Adults as well as students enjoy seeing how technology is used in the classroom. You could also have students work on current computer projects during the fair as a demonstration.

Have one class do just one booth or have all of the groups do *all* their booth ideas.

This is an ideal activity to use with your computer club.

This activity does not have to be used as a fund-raiser. Students can create a variety of booths to display at a middle school or a district-wide computer fair.

Name _____ Date _____

Fun with Fairs

The best thing about a school fair is that you get to have fun while earning money for your classroom, club, or school. The art students usually have a booth to sell pictures and pottery. The home economics students usually have a booth to sell cakes and cookies. The math students may offer number games to play. And the social studies students may read palms or crystal balls. But what can computer technology students do? Sell computers? You've got to be kidding! Well, why not? In fact, there are an abundant number of things you can do.

After your teacher has divided you into groups, start brainstorming for ideas. Make sure you keep track of all your ideas. You may change your minds later, or another group might need some help. For speed, use your word processor. All ideas for a fair booth must somehow be related to technology. Here is a list of booth ideas you can use if you wish:

- Collect donated computers and computer accessories and then sell them at the fair. This is a great way to recycle, and it's a tax deduction for the people who donate the computers.

- Write and sell a pamphlet on computer repair.

- Write and sell a pamphlet on how to buy a computer.

- Create and sell computer art (you could work with the art students on this booth idea).

- Using desktop publishing and drawing/painting software, create and sell calendars.

- Decide who is the best computer game player. Crown him/her the "Whiz Kid." People who come to your booth will have to pay to challenge the Whiz Kid at a computer game.

- Sell cookies shaped like a computer monitor, a mouse, a disk, and so on.

Once your group has come up with a list of ideas you would like to do, show the list to your teacher. With your teacher's help, choose the best booth idea.

Once you have an idea in place, do a little background research. How much will it cost to set up your booth? How long will it take to prepare for the booth? How many students will you need to create, set up, and run the booth? How many, and which, adults will be needed to supervise the whole operation? How much money do you believe you can make? When you have answered all vital questions, present your idea to the class. Taking into account the size and needs of the fair, the class chooses which booth ideas to use. Who knows, you might use them all.

Have fun at the fair!

61. Class Portfolio

Skills: Word processing, desktop publishing, drawing/painting, and/or stationery software use. Scanning graphic images and text pages. Linking graphic, text, sound (optional), and video (optional) files to a page in a multimedia presentation file.

Objectives: To create a class portfolio using small-group and large-group participation and as much computer technology as possible.

Level: Advanced.

Group Size: Initial group should be three to six students.

Time Required: Varies. Time is needed for research. Once all data are accumulated, it should take one day per group to scan all items. Scanned images (of graphics and text) should take two to three days to lay out in the multimedia presentation program.

Materials: At least one computer per group and a class scanner. Multimedia software such as HyperCard and HyperStudio for the Macintosh computer and Linkway and Toolbook for the PC computer. Word processing, drawing/painting, and desktop publishing software (helpful). Still video camera (optional) that stores pictures in the format that can easily be transferred into the computer in a graphic file format.

Procedure: Students create a class portfolio using multimedia software and scanning technology. Each small group is responsible for a section of the portfolio. They do research and collect vital information and then put that information into multimedia format. The use of a scanner is essential. This activity is designed for easy additions so that other classes can contribute to the portfolio.

Demonstration Needed: A demonstration of scanning techniques would be helpful.

Evaluation: Evaluate students based on group interaction and group end product.

Special Tips: Assign the research portion of the project well before it's time to scan images into the computer. Tell each group a minimum number of items they have to collect. Once all data are collected, allow each group to use the scanner on a rotational basis. While one group is using the scanner, the remaining groups are using software programs to create text or painting additions to the presentation. Do not start the activity until each group has collected the information to scan along with a detailed layout of the presentation.

Students can use databases to keep track of the type of information they have collected. You can study printouts to make sure all the students in the class are participating in the project.

Students can create survey sheets and use them during lunch periods to collect general information.

Technology is an important aspect of this activity. The whole point of using the computer is to save and add information easily. If you do not have the technology, this project may not be for you. However, students could still photocopy pictures and written information. Selling the portfolios at a later date would cover the printing cost.

Sound and video clip files can be added to most modern presentation programs. While most of these programs supply some sound files, students can download hundreds of additional sound files from bulletin board services. Linking video clips to a presentation is not difficult, but the process of making the video and storing it in a computer video format will add a lot of time to the project.

Cameras are on the market that take pictures and store them in a format that can easily be transferred into the computer as a full-screen image. The Apple QuickTake camera is very popular in schools today. These types of cameras are expensive but display clear pictures on computer screens with ease. Students can have fun using the camera at a sports game, a play, a dance, or any other school function. They can go around the school and take photos of all students who participate in school clubs and

(continued)

61. Class Portfolio *(continued)*

activities. The use of this type of camera is endless. It makes a great addition to any computer program.

As the year goes on and new classes enter your program, assign each class the job of locating and adding new information to the existing sections of the portfolio. For example, spring sports cannot be included in the portfolio with the fall classes. Therefore, by the end of the year, you will have a complete class portfolio containing facts and pictures about the entire school year.

Have students create their own portfolio that includes samples of their work from each class as well as pictures of their involvement in the school. Have each student start this portfolio during his or her first year at your school and add to it each year. Students can work in a cooperative learning setting to get classmates' opinions on what information to include in the portfolio and how to organize it. Students can also help each other use the different hardware and software needed to work on the project.

Name _____ Date _____

Class Portfolio

Yearbooks are good. But wouldn't it be great to have something that represented just your class, your grade? It will be a special day when you and your class graduate from middle school or junior high. It would be nice to have something that captured the memories of the last two or three years. Computers can help.

In this activity, small groups are responsible for putting together sections of a class portfolio. The portfolio will highlight the events and times of your class. It is designed for easy additions for later months and/or years.

As a group, decide which section of the portfolio you would like to work on. Most portfolios are made up of the following sections; however, feel free to add your own:

- Individual Student Photos and Biographies
- Clubs
- Sports
- Performing and Visual Arts
- Academic Excellence
- Current Events (inside and outside of school)
- Photos, Art, and Articles
- Teachers, Administrators, and Staff

Once your teacher has approved your choice, start collecting photographs and information about your peers. Be sure to keep track of whom the photos belong to by writing the owner's name on the back of each photo. Written information should be interesting and accurate. Anyone in the class can write articles, stories, and poems and can create drawings.

When you have finished collecting everything on your subject, start weeding through it. As a group, decide what should stay and what should go. Show your final collection to your teacher for approval.

Now comes the fun. Scan or transfer your collection into your computer by using multimedia software. This allows for easy additions and changes. Other groups can add their collection to yours. In the end, your complete class portfolio will be safely saved in the computer, just waiting for you to graduate.

Now what do you do with this portfolio? Here are some suggestions:

- At the graduation ceremony, dance, or dinner, run the multimedia presentation for all to enjoy.
- Make VHS copies of the multimedia presentation, or make a hard copy and photocopy it. Sell them at the end of the year to cover costs.